THE METHOD OF AVERAGING FUNCTIONAL CORRECTIONS

Theory and Applications

ACADEMIC PAPERBACKS*

EDITED BY Henry Booker, D. Allan Bromley, Nicholas DeClaris, W. Magnus, Alvin Nason, and A. Shenitzer

BIOLOGY

Design and Function at the Threshold of Life: The Viruses HEINZ FRAENKEL-CONRAT
The Evolution of Genetics ARNOLD W. RAVIN
Isotopes in Biology GEORGE WOLF
Life: Its Nature, Origin, and Development A. I. OPARIN
Time, Cells, and Aging BERNARD L. STREHLER

ENGINEERING

A Vector Approach to Oscillations HENRY BOOKER
Dynamic Programming and Modern Control Theory RICHARD BELLMAN and ROBERT KALABA

MATHEMATICS

Finite Permutation Groups HELMUT WIELANDT
Elements of Abstract Harmonic Analysis GEORGE BACHMAN
The Method of Averaging Functional Corrections: Theory and Applications A. YU. LUCHKA
Geometric Transformations (in two volumes) P. S. MODENOV and A. S. PARKHOMENKO
Representation Theory of Finite Groups MARTIN BURROW
Introduction to *p*-Adic Numbers and Valuation Theory GEORGE BACHMAN
Linear Operators in Hilbert Space WERNER SCHMEIDLER
Noneuclidean Geometry HERBERT MESCHKOWSKI
Quadratic Forms and Matrices N. V. YEFIMOV

PHYSICS

Crystals: Their Role in Nature and in Science CHARLES BUNN
Elementary Dynamics of Particles H. W. HARKNESS
Elementary Plane Rigid Dynamics H. W. HARKNESS
Mössbauer Effect: Principles and Applications GUNTHER K. WERTHEIM
Potential Barriers in Semiconductors B. R. GOSSICK
Principles of Vector Analysis JERRY B. MARION

*Most of these volumes are also available in a cloth bound edition.

THE METHOD OF AVERAGING FUNCTIONAL CORRECTIONS

Theory and Applications

By Anton Yur'yevich Luchka

Translated from the Russian by
SCRIPTA TECHNICA, Inc.

ACADEMIC PRESS New York and London

ACADEMIC PRESS INC.
111 Fifth Avenue, New York, New York 10003

United Kingdom Edition published by
ACADEMIC PRESS INC. (LONDON) LTD.
Berkeley Square House, London W.1.

LIBRARY OF CONGRESS CATALOG CARD NUMBER: 65-22776

PRINTED IN THE UNITED STATES OF AMERICA

First published in the Russian language under the title TEORIYA I PRIMENENIYE METODA OSREDNENIYA FUNKTSIONAL'NYKH POPRAVOK by the Academy of the Ukrainian S.S.R., Kiev, U.S.S.R., 1963.

Preface

The present work is devoted to investigations and generalizations of a new method of finding approximate solutions of integral, differential, integrodifferential, and other types of equations. This method was first suggested by Yu. D. Sokolov in 1952. In mathematical literature, it has come to be called "the method of averaging functional corrections."

The book consists of an introduction and four chapters.

In the introduction, a brief survey is given of the most widely used methods of approximate solution of the various types of equations. Also included is a short exposition of the original idea of the method of averaging functional corrections in connection with Fredholm's linear integral equations of the second kind.

The general theory of the method of averaging functional corrections as applied to linear equations in a Banach space is presented in the first chapter, in which a necessary and sufficient condition for convergence of the method is given. Various estimates of the error are presented, and comparison is made with the method of B. G. Galerkin.

In the second chapter, the method is applied to linear integral, differential, and integrodifferential equations. Various aspects of the method are shown and a number of examples illustrating its effectiveness are included. Some examples are solved by the method of averaging functional corrections as well as by other methods (such as the method of successive approximations, the method of moments, and Galerkin's method). Comparison of the results demonstrates the superiority of the method of averaging functional corrections over other approximation methods.

In the third chapter, the method of averaging functional corrections is applied to finite and infinite systems of linear integral and differential equations.

Finite and infinite systems of algebraic equations are solved by the method of averaging functional corrections in the fourth chapter, where effectiveness of the method is illustrated by examples.

As can be seen, the present work applies the method only to linear equations. However, it has been applied successfully to nonlinear equations of various types. The investigations of Yu. D. Sokolov and a number of works of other authors, for example, N. S. Kurpel', have been devoted to this question. Therefore, the present work serves as a supplement to Sokolov's monograph "Metod Osredneniya Funktsional'nykh Popravok" (The Method of Averaging Functional Corrections).

The author wishes to express his profound gratitude to the Member-Correspondant of the Academy of Sciences of the USSR, Yu. D. Sokolov, under whose supervision the present work was carried out, and to N. S. Kurpel' for valuable advice.

A. YU. LUCHKA

Contents

CHAPTER IV

Application of the Method to Systems of Linear Algebraic Equations

INTRODUCTION

The contemporary development of science and technology has considerably broadened the field of application of mathematics. In connection with this, the need for the development of approximate methods of solution of various mathematical problems has grown considerably.

There are many methods of approximate solution of differential, integral, and integrodifferential equations and systems of algebraic equations. These methods differ considerably in their effectiveness and in their range of application.

At the present time, difference methods, iteration methods and projection methods (the method of moments, the method of least squares, the Ritz-Galerkin method) are widely used. They are expounded in detail in the monographs of L. V. Kantorovich [14, 15], A. N. Krylov [25], N. M. Krylov [28], M. F. Kravchuk [19], L. Collatz [18], Sh. Ye. Mikeladze [47], S. G. Mikhlin [51, 54], Yu. V. Vorob'ev [7], I. S. Berezin and N. P. Zhidkov [2], and B. P. Demidovich, I. A. Maron, and E. Z. Shuvalova [10].

The most commonly used of the finite-difference methods is the method of nets, the theoretical investigation of which has been made in the work by R. Courant, K. Friedrichs, and H. Lewy [31]. As we know, to find an approximate solution by this method, we must solve a system of algebraic equations.

The method of nets can be applied to the solution of differential equations of arbitrary order with an arbitrary number of independent variables, and for that reason an extensive literature (see, for example, F. Bleykh and E. Melan [3], P. M. Varvak [5], L. A. Lyusternik [41, 42], G. Markus [44], I. O. Vlasov and I. A. Charnyi [6], I. G. Petrovskiy [61], and O. A.

Ladyzhenskaya [32]) has been written on the theory and application of this method from various points of view and with varying degrees of detail. The relative simplicity and the wide applicability of the method of nets has furthered its wide use.

In this connection, it should be noted that, although this method leads to simpler equations (to algebraic systems), increasing the accuracy of the approximations necessitates increasing the number of equations and hence the number of unknowns. Therefore, in practice, the method of nets can be applied only in those cases in which a sufficiently simple method of solving such systems is available. Special difficulties are encountered in applying the method to the solution of nonlinear equations.

The linear boundary value problems encountered in mathematical physics may usually be formulated as follows:

Let G be a region in m-dimensional Euclidean space. We denote the boundary of G by S. We are required to find a function $u(P)$ (where P is a point in the space) that is defined and sufficiently many times differentiable within G, and that satisfies the linear differential equation

$$Lu = f(P) \tag{1}$$

in this region and the boundary conditions

$$\Gamma_j u|_S = g_j(P) \qquad (j = 1, 2, \ldots, n) \tag{2}$$

on the boundary S.

In Eq. (1), $f(P)$ is a function defined in G. In Eq. (2), the linear operators $\Gamma_j u$ are generally differential operators, and the functions $g_j(P)$ are assumed given only on S.

If the operator Lu is positive definite, that is, if, for an arbitrary function $u(P)$ that is sufficiently many times continuously differentiable in the closed region $\bar{G} = G + S$ and satisfies Eqs. (2), the inequality

$$\int_G uLud\omega_P \geqslant \gamma^2 \int_G u^2 d\omega_P, \qquad \gamma > 0, u \not\equiv 0,$$

holds, then the problem of integrating Eq. (1) under the boundary conditions (2) is equivalent to the problem of finding the minimum of the functional

$$F(u) = \int_G \{uLu - 2uf\}\, d\omega_P \tag{3}$$

under the same boundary conditions. Under such conditions, the problem of the minimum of the functional (3) has a solution that can be constructed by the Ritz method.

The idea behind the Ritz method [64] is that an approximate solution is sought in the form

$$u_n(P) = \sum_{k=1}^{n} a_k \varphi_k(P), \tag{4}$$

where $\varphi_1(P)$, $\varphi_2(P)$, ..., $\varphi_n(P)$ – n are the first n functions of a complete system of linearly independent functions satisfying the boundary conditions (2).

The parameters a_k are chosen in such a way that the functional $F(u_n)$ will take its minimum value; that is, to determine the parameters a_k, we obtain the system of equations

$$\frac{\partial F(u_n)}{\partial a_k} = 0 \qquad (k = 1, 2, \ldots, n).$$

The Ritz method has been investigated in the works of N. M. Krylov [26, 27], N. M. Krylov and N. N. Bogolyubov [29], R. Courant and D. Hilbert [30], V. I. Smirnov [67], M. Picone [62], L. V. Kantorovich [12], S. G. Mikhlin [52], and others. The article by Kantorovich [11] gives a development of the Ritz method.

More general than the method of Ritz is the method of Galerkin [8].

The essential feature of this method consists in the fact that an approximate solution is again sought in the form (4) but with the constants a_k determined from the condition of orthogonality of the function

$$\varepsilon_n(P) = Lu_n(P) - f(P)$$

to the chosen functions $\varphi_k(P)$:

$$\int_G \varepsilon_n(P)\varphi_k(P)\, d\omega_p = 0 \qquad (k = 1, 2, \ldots, n).$$

In the case of a self-conjugate problem, the Ritz and Galerkin methods coincide.

The Galerkin method has come to be used widely and has been applied to a number of different problems. A detailed bibliography on the question of the applications of this method is included in the survey article by Ya. I. Perel'man [59].

The convergence of the Galerkin method in a single particular problem was first shown by G. I. Petrov [60].

General results pertaining to the convergence of the approximate solutions obtained by the Galerkin method were first obtained by M. V. Keldysh [17], whose work is based on a study of infinite determinants. In later works by L. V. Kantorovich [13], S. G. Mikhlin [48, 49], N. I. Pol'skiy [63], and M. A. Krasnosel'skiy [21, 22], the methods of functional analysis were applied to the investigation of the convergence of the Galerkin method. In these last works, the investigation usually consisted in a study of completely continuous operators, both linear and nonlinear. In those of Pol'skiy and Krasnosel'skiy, general estimates of the speed of convergence of the approximate solutions obtained by the Galerkin method are given.

However, in the case of nonlinear equations, the solution of practical problems by the Galerkin method presents considerable difficulty, as was noted in the article [21], because here one must deal with a system of transcendental equations that is just as hard to solve as the original problem.

The method of least squares can be used to solve many problems. In a number of cases, this method gives a better convergence of the approximations than does the Ritz method. In some of their works, N. M. Krylov and N. N. Bogolyubov applied the method of least squares to finding an approximate solution of differential and integral equations.

The essential feature of this method when applied to the problem (1)–(2) is that an approximate solution is sought in the form (4), and the parameters a_k are determined from the condition that the functional

$$\int_G (Lu_n - f)^2 \, d\omega_P$$

be minimized.

As a result, we arrive at a system of n algebraic equations with n unknowns.

The works of S. G. Mikhlin [50, 53] are devoted to a theoretical study of the method of least squares.

The monograph of L. S. Leybenzon [33] gives the solutions of certain specific problems in the theory of elasticity by the method of least squares. A number of problems to which the method of least squares is applied are analyzed in [54].

M. F. Kravchuk [20] studied the method of least squares as a particular case of the general method of moments.

The application of the method of moments to linear differential and integral equations is investigated in detail in [19].

The application of the method of moments to the problem (1)–(2) consists in seeking an approximate solution in the form (4) and determining the parameters a_k from the condition that the result of the substitution of u_n in the expression $Lu - f(P)$ be orthogonal to the first n functions of some other system of linearly independent functions $\{\psi_k(P)\}$:

$$\int_G (Lu_n - f)\psi_k(P) \, d\omega_P = 0 \qquad (k = 1, 2, \ldots, n).$$

If $\varphi_k(P) = \psi_k(P)$, this reduces to the Galerkin method.

With all these methods (Ritz, Galerkin, moments, least squares) greater accuracy is attained by increasing n. However, it may happen that for $n_2 > n_1$, the approximation $u_{n_2}(P)$ will be considerably worse than the approximation $u_{n_1}(P)$. This does not happen in the case of a convergent iteration method; here successive approximations always improve in accuracy.

The idea of using the method of successive approximations (the iteration method) for solving various equations arose many years ago. It was already used by Liouville [34] in his studies on linear differential equations. The same method was used by Neumann [56] in his studies of potential theory.

For various types of equations, the method of successive approximations falls into the general framework of functional analysis and leads to the principle of contraction mappings (see, for example, V. V. Nemytskiy [57], L. A. Lyusternik and V. I. Sobolev [43], and L. V. Kantorovich and G. P. Akilov [15]) formulated in 1922 by the Polish mathematician S. Banach [1] and first used to prove the existence theorems of Caccioppoli [16] in 1930.

Consider the equation

$$x = f + \lambda A x, \tag{5}$$

where A is a linear operator in a Banach space E, λ is a complex parameter, f is a given element of the space E, and x is the desired unknown element of the space E.

The principle of the method of successive approximations consists in starting with an arbitrary element $x_0 \in E$ (the initial approximation) and using it to construct a sequence $\{x_n\}$ of approximate solutions

$$x_n = f + \lambda A x_{n-1} \qquad (n = 1, 2, 3, \ldots). \tag{6}$$

The convergence of the sequence of approximations (6) for Eq. (5) is shown to be closely connected with the convergence of the series

$$I + \lambda A + \lambda^2 A^2 + \cdots + \lambda^n A^n + \cdots, \tag{7}$$

the radius of convergence of which is given by the formula

$$r = \frac{1}{\lim\limits_{n\to\infty} \sqrt[n]{\|A^n\|}}.$$

The sum of the series (7) (when that series converges) is $(I - \lambda A)^{-1}$.

From this it is clear that a sequence of approximations may not converge to the solution. This fact considerably restricts the number of problems for which the method of approximations can be used. Even if a sequence of approximations converges to the solution, it often happens that the convergence is so slow that, in practice, one needs to perform a very large number of calculations to get a sufficiently accurate solution.

These restrictions on the range of applicability and the slowness of convergence of the approximations temporarily dampened interest in the theory of iteration methods. Only recently, with the appearance of computing machines, have iteration methods, as a result of the simplicity of the computational scheme, come to be widely used in practical computations. In connection with this, various methods for speeding up the convergence of iteration processes have been developed in recent years. These methods make it possible to extend the number of problems that can be solved by iteration methods and to decrease the number of calculations. One of them is the method of averaging functional corrections, developed by Yu. D. Sokolov.

Let us show briefly what the crux of Sokolov's method (developed in [68–76]) is. We shall illustrate the idea behind the method for the linear Fredholm integral equation of the second kind

$$y(x) = f(x) + \lambda \int_a^b K(x, \xi) y(\xi)\, d\xi \qquad (0 < |\lambda| < \infty). \tag{8}$$

As our first approximation, we take

$$y_1(x) = f(x) + \lambda \alpha_1 \int_a^b K(x, \xi)\, d\xi, \tag{9}$$

where

$$\alpha_1 = \frac{1}{h} \int_a^b y_1(x)\, dx \qquad (h = b - a > 0). \tag{10}$$

From Eqs. (9) and (10), we determine α_1,

$$\alpha_1 = \frac{1}{D(\lambda)} \int_a^b f(x)\, dx, \tag{11}$$

where

$$D(\lambda) = h - \lambda \int_a^b \int_a^b K(x, \xi)\, d\xi\, dx.$$

As our nth approximation, we take

$$y_n(x) = f(x) + \lambda \int_a^b K(x, \xi)\{y_{n-1}(\xi) + \alpha_n\}\, d\xi, \tag{12}$$

where

$$\alpha_n = \frac{1}{h} \int_a^b \delta_n(x)\, dx, \tag{13}$$

$$\delta_n(x) = y_n(x) - y_{n-1}(x) \qquad (n = 2, 3, \ldots). \tag{14}$$

On the basis of Eqs. (12), (13), and (14), we obtain

$$\alpha_n = \frac{\lambda}{D(\lambda)} \int_a^b \int_a^b K(x, \xi)\{\delta_{n-1}(\xi) - \alpha_{n-1}\}\, d\xi\, dx.$$

The method applied in this form is simple from a computational point of view.

L. E. Krivoshein [23, 24] applied Sokolov's method to solving boundary-value problems and the Cauchy problem for linear integrodifferential equations.

In somewhat modified form, this method was applied to linear integral equations by Yu. M. Molokovich [45].

V. Kh. Sirenko [66] worked on numerical methods involving the use of Sokolov's method.

E. A. Chernyshenko [77, 78] submitted an algorithm generalizing Sokolov's algorithm. However, the sufficient conditions for convergence of the sequence constructed by his algorithm are too restricted. For example, for integral equation (8) in the space $L^2(a, b)$, the sufficient condition given in [78] fails to guarantee convergence not only for the values of λ at which the usual method of successive approximations diverges but even for those values of λ at which the latter converges. However, sufficient conditions are given in [35] and [36] that guarantee convergence in the mean of the sequence (12) to the solution of the integral equation (8) for values of λ at which the usual method of successive approximations diverges.

In conclusion, we note that, in the works of Yu. D. Sokolov [72, 74, 75] and B. G. Mosolov [46], the method of averaging functional corrections is applied to nonlinear integral, differential, and integrodifferential equations. E. A. Chernyshenko [78] has applied this method to nonlinear operator equations in a complete normed space.

CHAPTER I

The General Theory of the Method

In the present chapter, we shall examine the equation

$$x = f + \lambda A x \tag{1.1}$$

in a complex Banach space E. Here, A is a linear operator, λ is a complex parameter, f is a given element, and x is the desired unknown element of the space E. Equations that can be reduced to equations of the form (1.1) will also be examined.

We shall solve Eq. (1) by Sokolov's method, the essentials of which will be expounded below.

1. Construction of the Algorithm

As was said in the introduction, the principle behind the Sokolov method consists in the following: Suppose that x_0 is an arbitrary element of the space E. Then, as our first approximation, we take

$$x_1 = f + \lambda A(x_0 + \alpha_1), \tag{1.2}$$

where

$$\alpha_1 = P\delta_1, \tag{1.3}$$

$$\delta_1 = x_1 - x_0, \tag{1.4}$$

where P is a projection operator projecting the space E onto its subspace $\tilde{E}$. (If the space $\tilde{E}$ is finite dimensional, we shall write P_K instead of P.)

When we substitute Eq. (1.2) in Eq. (1.4), we obtain

$$\delta_1 = \varepsilon_0 + \lambda A \alpha_1 , \tag{1.5}$$

where

$$\varepsilon_0 = f - x_0 + \lambda A x_0 .$$

On the basis of formulas (1.3) and (1.5), we obtain an equation for determining the element α_1:

$$\alpha_1 = P\varepsilon_0 + \lambda PA\alpha_1 . \tag{1.6}$$

Let us assume the existence of the bounded inverse operator $(I - \lambda PA)^{-1}$. Then, from Eq. (1.6), we obtain

$$\alpha_1 = (I - \lambda PA)^{-1} P\varepsilon_0 . \tag{1.7}$$

Thus, our first approximation is completely determined. If the $(n-1)$st approximation is determined, then we define the nth approximation by

$$x_n = f + \lambda A(x_{n-1} + \alpha_n), \tag{1.8}$$

where

$$\alpha_n = P\delta_n , \tag{1.9}$$

$$\delta_n = x_n - x_{n-1} . \tag{1.10}$$

On the basis of (1.8) and (1.10), we have

$$\delta_n = \varepsilon_{n-1} + \lambda A\alpha_n , \tag{1.11}$$

where

$$\varepsilon_{n-1} = f - x_{n-1} + \lambda A x_{n-1} . \tag{1.12}$$

When we substitute the value of α_n given by Eq. (1.11) in Eq. (1.9), we obtain the equation for determining α_n :

$$\alpha_n = P\varepsilon_{n-1} + \lambda PA\alpha_n . \tag{1.13}$$

From Eq. (1.13), we obtain

$$\alpha_n = (I - \lambda PA)^{-1} P\varepsilon_{n-1} . \tag{1.14}$$

If we substitute (1.14) in (1.8), we finally obtain the formula for determining the nth approximation:

$$x_n = f + \lambda A x_{n-1} + \lambda A(I - \lambda PA)^{-1} P\varepsilon_{n-1} \quad (n = 1, 2, 3, \ldots). \tag{1.15}$$

Let us consider the case in which the subspace $\tilde{E}$ is finite dimensional of dimension k. Every element $\tilde{y} \in \tilde{E}$ can be uniquely represented in the form

$$\tilde{y} = c_1\varphi_1 + c_2\varphi_2 + \cdots + c_k\varphi_k,$$

where the elements $\varphi_1, \varphi_2, \ldots, \varphi_k$ constitute a basis in the subspace $\tilde{E}$.

Let us define a complete system of functionals $f_1, f_2, \ldots, f_k$ on $\tilde{E}$, that is, a system such that the equations $f_i(\tilde{y}) = 0$ (for $i = 1, 2, \ldots, k$) imply that $\tilde{y} = 0$. Then, Eq. (1.9) takes the form

$$\alpha_n = P_k\delta_n = c_{n_1}\varphi_1 + c_{n_2}\varphi_2 + \cdots + c_{n_k}\varphi_k, \tag{1.16}$$

and Eq. (1.13) becomes equivalent to the system of equations

$$f_i(\alpha_n - \lambda P_k A\alpha_n) = f_i(P_k\varepsilon_{n-1}) \qquad (i = 1, 2, \ldots, k). \tag{1.17}$$

If we substitute the value of α_n given by formula (1.16) in Eq. (1.17), we obtain a finite system of linear algebraic equations defining c_{ni}:

$$\sum_{j=1}^{k} (\gamma_{ij} - \lambda K_{ij})c_{nj} = b_{ni} \qquad (i = 1, 2, \ldots, k; \quad n = 1, 2, 3, \ldots), \tag{1.18}$$

where

$$\gamma_{ij} = f_i(\varphi_j), \qquad K_{ij} = f_i(P_k A\varphi_j), \qquad b_{ni} = f_i(P_k\varepsilon_{n-1}).$$

When the system of functionals $f_1, f_2, \ldots, f_k$ is biorthogonal to the basis $\varphi_1, \varphi_2, \ldots, \varphi_k$, that is, when $f_i(\varphi_j) = \delta_{ij}$, the system (1.18) is simplified, acquiring the form

$$c_{ni} = b_{ni} + \lambda \sum_{j=1}^{k} K_{ij}c_{nj} \qquad (i = 1, 2, \ldots, k; \quad n = 1, 2, 3, \ldots), \tag{1.19}$$

and now,

$$K_{ij} = f_i(A\varphi_j), \qquad b_{ni} = f_i(\varepsilon_{n-1}).$$

If in addition $x_0 = \theta$, we obtain an algorithm first presented by E. A. Chernyshenko in [78].

2. A Necessary and Sufficient Condition for Convergence of the Method. Neumann's Series

On the basis of Eqs. (1.9) and (1.10), Eq. (1.8) can be represented in the form

$$x_n = f + \lambda A x_{n-1} + \lambda AP(x_n - x_{n-1}),$$

or

$$x_n = f + \lambda AQx_{n-1} + \lambda APx_n, \tag{1.20}$$

where

$$Q = I - P$$

(I is the identity operator).

If there exists a bounded inverse operator $(I - \lambda AP)^{-1}$, we have, from Eq. (1.20),

$$x_n = (I - \lambda AP)^{-1}f + \lambda(I - \lambda AP)^{-1}AQx_{n-1}, \tag{1.21}$$

or

$$x_n = f^* + \Omega_\lambda x_{n-1}, \tag{1.22}$$

where

$$\Omega_\lambda = \lambda(I - \lambda AP)^{-1}AQ.$$

Equation (1.20) can also be solved in the following manner. If we apply the operator P to Eq. (1.20) from the left, we get

$$Px_n = Pf + \lambda PAQx_{n-1} + \lambda PAPx_n,$$

so that

$$Px_n = (I - \lambda PA)^{-1}\{Pf + \lambda PAQx_{n-1}\}. \tag{1.23}$$

When we substitute this in Eq. (1.20), we obtain

$$x_n = f + \lambda AQx_{n-1} + \lambda A(I - \lambda PA)^{-1}Pf + \lambda^2 A(I - \lambda PA)^{-1}PAQx_{n-1}. \tag{1.24}$$

By relatively simple transformations, we obtain

$$\lambda(I - \lambda PA)^{-1}PA = (I - \lambda PA)^{-1} - I. \tag{1.25}$$

Indeed,

$$\begin{aligned}\lambda(I - \lambda PA)^{-1}PA &= (I - \lambda PA)^{-1}(\lambda PA - I + I)\\ &= (I - \lambda PA)^{-1} - (I - \lambda PA)^{-1}(I - \lambda PA)\\ &= (I - \lambda PA)^{-1} - I.\end{aligned}$$

In view of (1.25), Eq. (1.24) takes the form

$$x_n = f + \lambda A(I - \lambda PA)^{-1}Pf + \lambda A(I - \lambda PA)^{-1}Qx_{n-1}. \quad (1.26)$$

By equating the right-hand sides of Eqs. (1.21) and (1.26), we obtain

$$f^* = (I - \lambda AP)^{-1}f = f + \lambda A(I - \lambda PA)^{-1}Pf, \quad (1.27)$$

$$\Omega_\lambda = \lambda(I - \lambda AP)^{-1}AQ = \lambda A(I - \lambda PA)^{-1}Q. \quad (1.28)$$

The operator Ω_λ satisfies the equation

$$\Omega_\lambda = \lambda AQ + \lambda AP\Omega_\lambda. \quad (1.29)$$

To see this, we substitute the value of Ω_λ given by formula (1.28) in the right-hand member of Eq. (1.29) and, by using Eq. (1.25), we obtain

$$\begin{aligned} \lambda AQ + \lambda AP\Omega_\lambda &= \lambda AQ + \lambda^2 APA(I - \lambda PA)^{-1}Q \\ &= \lambda AQ + \lambda A(I - \lambda PA)^{-1}Q - \lambda AQ \\ &= \lambda A(I - \lambda PA)^{-1}Q = \Omega_\lambda. \end{aligned}$$

It is clear from (1.28) that if one of the operators $(I - \lambda AP)^{-1}$ or $(I - \lambda PA)^{-1}$ exists, so does the other.

The sequence (1.15) can easily be reduced to the form (1.22). Specifically, by substituting Eq. (1.12) in Eq. (1.15), we obtain

$$\begin{aligned} x_n &= f + \lambda Ax_{n-1} + \lambda A(I - \lambda PA)^{-1}P(f - x_{n-1} + \lambda Ax_{n-1}) \\ &= f + \lambda A(I - \lambda PA)^{-1}Pf + \lambda Ax_{n-1} \\ &\quad - \lambda A(I - \lambda PA)^{-1}Px_{n-1} + \lambda^2 A(I - \lambda PA)^{-1}PAx_{n-1}. \end{aligned}$$

By using Eq. (1.25) and formulas (1.27) and (1.28), we finally obtain

$$\begin{aligned} x_n &= f^* + \lambda Ax_{n-1} - \lambda A(I - \lambda PA)^{-1}Px_{n-1} \\ &\quad + \lambda A\{(I - \lambda PA)^{-1} - I\}x_{n-1} \\ &= f^* + \lambda A(I - \lambda PA)^{-1}(x_{n-1} - Px_{n-1}) \\ &= f^* + \lambda A(I - \lambda PA)^{-1}Qx_{n-1} = f^* + \Omega_\lambda x_{n-1}. \end{aligned}$$

If we replace x_{n-1} in Eq. (1.22) by its value given by an equation analogous to (1.22), we obtain

$$\begin{aligned} x_n &= f^* + \Omega_\lambda(f^* + \Omega_\lambda x_{n-2}) \\ &= f^* + \Omega_\lambda f^* + \Omega_\lambda \Omega_\lambda x_{n-2}. \end{aligned}$$

From the obvious relationship $Q^2 = Q$, we obtain

$$\begin{aligned} x_n &= f^* + \Omega_\lambda f^* + \Omega_\lambda Q \Omega_\lambda x_{n-2} \\ &= f^* + \Omega_\lambda f^* + \Omega_\lambda L_\lambda x_{n-2}, \end{aligned} \tag{1.30}$$

where

$$L_\lambda = Q\Omega_\lambda. \tag{1.31}$$

If we substitute in Eq. (1.31) the value of Ω_λ given by Eq. (1.28), we obtain

$$L_\lambda = \lambda Q(I - \lambda AP)^{-1}AQ = \lambda QA(I - \lambda PA)^{-1}Q. \tag{1.32}$$

By continuing this process, that is, by replacing x_{n-2} in Eq. (1.30) with its value given by a formula analogous to Eq. (1.22) and so on, we obtain

$$\begin{aligned} x_n = f^* + \Omega_\lambda f^* + \Omega_\lambda L_\lambda f^* + \Omega_\lambda L_\lambda{}^2 f^* \\ + \cdots + \Omega_\lambda L_\lambda^{n-2} f^* + \Omega_\lambda L_\lambda^{n-1} x_0. \end{aligned} \tag{1.33}$$

Since Eqs. (1.15) and (1.33) represent the same sequence but in different forms, the question of convergence of the sequence (1.15) is reduced to the question of the convergence of sequence (1.33). Now, the convergence of the sequence (1.33) is closely connected with the convergence of the series

$$I + L_\lambda + L_\lambda{}^2 + \cdots + L_\lambda{}^n + \cdots. \tag{1.34}$$

It may happen that our first approximation already gives the exact solution. This can happen only in the case (excluding the case of $x_0 = x^*$) in which $x_0 = \theta$ and $AQx^* = \theta$, where x^* is the exact solution of Eq. (1.1).

THEOREM 1. *If there exists a bounded inverse operator* $(I - \lambda AP)^{-1}$ *and if, for some n, the inequality*

$$\|L_\lambda{}^n\| < 1, \tag{1.35}$$

is satisfied, then for arbitrary $f \in E$, *there exists a unique solution to Eq.* (1.1) *and the sequence* (1.15) *converges to that solution.*

Condition (1.35) *is necessary and sufficient for the convergence of the Sokolov method.*

Proof. Equation (1.1) can be replaced by the system of equations

$$x = f^* + Q_\lambda y, \tag{1.36}$$

$$y = Qf^* + L_\lambda y. \tag{1.37}$$

In fact, if we apply the operator $(I - \lambda AP)^{-1}$ to the equation

$$x = f + \lambda Ax = f + \lambda APx + \lambda AQx,$$

we obtain

$$x = (I - \lambda AP)^{-1}f + \lambda(I - \lambda AP)^{-1}AQx. \tag{1.38}$$

On the basis of formulas (1.27) and (1.28), Eq. (1.38) takes the form

$$x = f^* + \Omega_\lambda x. \tag{1.39}$$

If we set $y = Qx$, we obtain from (1.39) Eqs. (1.36) and (1.37).

It is clear from the system of Eqs. (1.36) and (1.37) that if x^* is a solution of Eq. (1.1) then $y^* = Qx^*$ is a solution of Eq. (1.37) and, conversely, if $\tilde{y}$ is a solution of Eq. (1.37), then

$$x^* = f^* + \Omega_\lambda \tilde{y} \tag{1.40}$$

is a solution of Eq. (1.1).

We conclude that the question of the existence and uniqueness of a solution to Eq. (1.1) reduces to the question of the existence and uniqueness of a solution of Eq. (1.37).

We shall solve Eq. (1.37) by the method of successive approximations. If we take for our initial approximation the element $y_0 = Qx_0 \in E$, then the $(n - 1)$st approximation will be of the form

$$\tilde{y}_{n-1} = (I + L_\lambda + L_\lambda{}^2 + \cdots + L_\lambda^{n-2})f^* + L_\lambda^{n-1}x_0. \tag{1.41}$$

Then, the nth approximation of Eq. (1.36) will be given by the formula

$$\tilde{x}_n = f^* + \Omega_\lambda \tilde{y}_{n-1}$$
$$= f^* + \Omega_\lambda L_\lambda^{n-1} x_0 + \Omega_\lambda (I + L_\lambda + L_\lambda^2 + \cdots + L_\lambda^{n-2}) f^*. \tag{1.42}$$

Comparing formulas (1.33) and (1.42), we note that $\tilde{x}_n = x_n$. Consequently, we can obtain the sequence (1.15) if we substitute in Eq. (1.36) the $(n-1)$st approximation $\tilde{y}_{n-1}$ of Eq. (1.37).

Let us assume that the series (1.34) converges. Then the sequence (1.41) obviously has a limit

$$\tilde{y} = \lim_{n\to\infty} \tilde{y}_{n-1} = \sum_{n=0}^{\infty} L_\lambda^n f^* = (I - L_\lambda)^{-1} f^*, \tag{1.43}$$

since $L_\lambda^{n-1} x_0 \to \theta$, as $n \to \infty$, and this limit $\tilde{y}$ is the unique solution of Eq. (1.37). Consequently, on the basis of Eq. (1.40), x^* is also the unique solution of Eq. (1.1).

If we substitute Eq. (1.43) in Eq. (1.40), the solution x^* of Eq. (1.1) will take the form

$$x^* = f^* + \sum_{n=0}^{\infty} \Omega_\lambda L_\lambda^n f^* = f^* + \Omega_\lambda (I - L_\lambda)^{-1} f^*. \tag{1.44}$$

We obtain this same equation if we pass directly to the limit in Eq. (1.42) or in Eq. (1.33), which is its equivalent. But passing to the limit in Eq. (1.33) is equivalent to passing to the limit in Eq. (1.15). Consequently, if the series (1.34) converges, then the sequence (1.15) converges to the solution of Eq. (1.1).

Reference [15] (see pp. 153, 154) proves a theorem on the basis of which

$$\Lambda(\lambda) = \lim_{n\to\infty} \sqrt[n]{\|L_\lambda^n\|} = \inf_n \sqrt[n]{\|L_\lambda^n\|} < \infty. \tag{1.45}$$

Here, the series (1.34) converges if $\Lambda(\lambda) < 1$.

Keeping this in mind, we shall show that condition (1.35) is necessary and sufficient for convergence of the series (1.34). If the series (1.34) converges, it is necessary that $\|L_\lambda^n\| \to 0$ and therefore, condition (1.35) is satisfied for sufficiently large n. Conversely, if condition (1.35) holds, then

$$\Lambda(\lambda) = \inf_n \sqrt[n]{\|L_\lambda^n\|} \leqslant \sqrt[n]{\|L_\lambda^n\|} < 1,$$

and hence the series (1.34) converges.

Thus, condition (1.35) is necessary and sufficient for the convergence of the Sokolov method.

We call attention to the fact that in the case of $P = 0$ the method degenerates into the usual process of successive approximations. In this case, $\Omega_\lambda = L_\lambda = \lambda A$ and $f^* = f$. Consequently, the series (1.44) takes the form

$$x^* = f + \sum_{n=0}^{\infty} \lambda^{n+1} A^{n+1} f. \tag{1.46}$$

The series (1.46) is known in the literature as Neumann's series. Since it is a particular case of the series (1.44), we shall call the latter series "Neumann's series for the Sokolov method."

From the fact that x^* is a solution of Eq. (1.1), that is, from the fact that

$$\begin{aligned}(I - \lambda A)x^* &= (I - \lambda A)\{I + \Omega_\lambda(I - L_\lambda)^{-1}\}f^* \\ &= (I - \lambda A)\{I + \Omega_\lambda(I - L_\lambda)^{-1}\}(I - \lambda AP)^{-1}f = f,\end{aligned}$$

it follows that

$$\begin{aligned}(I - \lambda A)^{-1} &= \{I + \Omega_\lambda(I - L_\lambda)^{-1}\}(I - \lambda AP)^{-1} \\ &= (I - \lambda AP)^{-1} + \sum_{n=0}^{\infty} \Omega_\lambda L_\lambda^n (I - \lambda AP)^{-1}.\end{aligned} \tag{1.47}$$

Theorem 1 has the following corollary:

COROLLARY 1. *For convergence of the Sokolov method, it is sufficient that*

$$L(\lambda) < 1, \qquad \text{where} \qquad L(\lambda) = \|L_\lambda\|. \tag{1.48}$$

The method does indeed converge under this condition since then

$$\Lambda(\lambda) = \inf_n \sqrt[n]{\|L_\lambda{}^n\|} \leqslant \sqrt[n]{\|L_\lambda{}^n\|} \leqslant \sqrt[n]{\|L_\lambda\|^n} = \|L_\lambda\| = L(\lambda) < 1. \tag{1.49}$$

Suppose that G is the set of regular points of the operator A, that is, suppose that G consists of those values of λ for which there exists a bounded inverse operator $(I - \lambda A)^{-1}$. Suppose that G^* is the set of spectral points of the operator A, that is, suppose that G^* consists of those values of λ for which there is no bounded inverse operator. Suppose that $G_P{}^*$ is the set of spectral points of the operator AP. Suppose, finally, that M, M^*, N, and N^* are sets of values of λ for which

$$L(\lambda) < 1, \qquad L(\lambda) \geqslant 1, \qquad \Lambda(\lambda) < 1, \qquad \Lambda(\lambda) \geqslant 1,$$

respectively. Obviously, $N^* \bigcap G_P{}^*$ is the empty set.

Under these conditions, the following theorem applies:

THEOREM 2. *The set of spectral points G^* of the operator A is contained in the set $N^* + G_P{}^*$ and the set of regular points G of the operator A contains the set N. In symbols,*

$$G^* \subset N^* + G_P{}^*, \qquad G \supset N.$$

Proof. The set N consists only of regular points. To see this, let us assume the opposite, that is, that for $\lambda_0 \in G^*$ the condition $\Lambda(\lambda_0) < 1$ holds. Then, the series (1.47) converges; that is, there exists an inverse operator $(I - \lambda_0 A)^{-1}$. This is a contradiction since for $\lambda_0 \in G^*$ no bounded inverse operator exists. Consequently,

$$N \subset G.$$

Since the set N does not contain spectral points, these must belong to the set $N^* + G_P{}^*$; that is,

$$G^* \subset N^* + G_P{}^*.$$

COROLLARY 2. *This is true*

$$G^* \subset M^* + G_P{}^*, \qquad G \supset M.$$

From the inequality [see inequality (1.49)]

$$\Lambda(\lambda) \leqslant L(\lambda)$$

and from the obvious relationship

$$G + G^* = N + N^* + G_P{}^* = M + M^* + G_P{}^*$$

we have

$$N \supset M, \qquad N^* \subset M^*.$$

Consequently, on the basis of Theorem 2,

$$G \supset N \supset M,$$

$$G^* \subset N^* + G_P{}^* \subset M^* + G_P{}^*.$$

COROLLARY 3. *If λ^* belongs to the spectrum, that is, if $\lambda^* \in G^*$, the sequence* (1.15) *either does not converge or, in general, cannot be constructed.*

Proof. Since $\lambda^* \in G^*$, it follows from Theorem 2 that $\lambda^* \in N^* + G_P{}^*$. From this it is clear that λ^* belongs to the set $G_P{}^*$ or to the set N^*. If $\lambda^* \in N^*$, the inequality $\Lambda(\lambda^*) \geqslant 1$ holds, which guarantees divergence of the series (1.34); that is, the sequence (1.15) does not converge to the solution of Eq. (1.1). On the other hand, if $\lambda^* \in G_P{}^*$, the inverse operator $(I - \lambda^* AP)^{-1}$ either does not exist or is unbounded. Consequently, we cannot construct successive approximations of the form (1.15).

Note. All the above applies also to more general equations of the form

$$x = f + A_\lambda x \tag{1.50}$$

under the assumption that the linear operator A_λ, which depends on the complex parameter λ, operates in a complex Banach space E and is defined for all values of λ belonging to some set G.

3. The Case of a Completely Continuous Operator

Let us study certain properties of the method under the assumption that A is a completely continuous operator.

In the case of a finite-dimensional subspace $\tilde{E}$, the operators Ω_λ and L_λ, their norms $\Omega(\lambda)$ and $L(\lambda)$, and also the sets M, M^*, N, and N^* depend in a definite way on the dimension of the subspace $\tilde{E}$. In order not to lose sight of this, we shall, in what follows, adhere to the following notations for such a case:

$$\Omega_{k\lambda}, \quad L_{k\lambda}, \quad \Omega_k(\lambda), \quad L_k(\lambda), \quad M_k, \quad M_k^*, \quad N_k \quad \text{and} \quad N_k^*.$$

THEOREM 3. *If* (1) *an operator A is completely continuous,* (2) *λ is its regular value, and* (3) $P_k \to I$ as $k \to \infty$, *then,*

$$L_k(\lambda) \to 0,$$

as $k \to \infty$, where

$$L_k(\lambda) = \|L_{k\lambda}\| = \|\lambda Q_k A(I - \lambda P_k A)^{-1} Q_k\| \qquad (Q_k = I - P_k).$$

Proof. The operator $L_{k\lambda}$ can be represented in the form

$$L_{k\lambda} = Q_k(I - \lambda A)\{(I - \lambda A)^{-1} - (I - \lambda P_k A)^{-1}\} Q_k. \quad (1.51)$$

This is true, since

$$\begin{aligned} L_{k\lambda} &= \lambda Q_k A(I - \lambda P_k A)^{-1} Q_k + Q_k - Q_k \\ &= \lambda Q_k A(I - \lambda P_k A)^{-1} Q_k + Q_k(I - \lambda A)(I - \lambda A)^{-1} Q_k \\ &\quad - Q_k(I - \lambda P_k A)(I - \lambda P_k A)^{-1} Q_k \\ &= Q_k(I - \lambda A)\{(I - \lambda A)^{-1} - (I - \lambda P_k A)^{-1}\} Q_k. \end{aligned}$$

It is shown in [13] that if A is a completely continuous operator and λ is its regular value, that is, if there exists a bounded inverse operator $(I - \lambda A)^{-1}$, then for sufficiently large k there always exists a bounded inverse operator $(I - \lambda P_k A)^{-1}$ and

$$\|(I - \lambda A)^{-1} - (I - \lambda P_k A)^{-1}\| \to 0 \quad (1.52)$$

as $k \to \infty$.

From Eq. (1.51), we obtain

$$\|L_{k\lambda}\| \leqslant \|Q_k(I - \lambda A)\| \cdot \|(I - \lambda A)^{-1} - (I - \lambda P_k A)^{-1}\| \cdot \|Q_k\|.$$

Consequently, on the basis of the hypothesis of the theorem and the relation (1.52), we have

$$L_k(\lambda) \to 0 \qquad \text{as} \qquad k \to \infty.$$

Theorem 3 has the following corollaries:

COROLLARY 4. *If A is a completely continuous operator and λ is a regular value of A, then,*

$$L_k(\lambda) \to 0 \qquad \text{as} \qquad k \to \infty,$$

where

$$\Lambda_k(\lambda) = \lim_{n \to \infty} \sqrt[n]{\|L_{k\lambda}^n\|} \leqslant L_k(\lambda).$$

COROLLARY 5. *If A is a continuous operator and λ is its regular value, then it is always possible to choose a projection operator P_k so that $L_k(\lambda) < 1$, which ensures convergence of the method.*

On the basis of Theorems 2 and 3 and Corollaries 2 and 4, for an arbitrary k, we have

$$G \supset N_k \supset M_k, \qquad G^* \subset N_k{}^* + G_{P_k}^* \subset M_k{}^* + G_{P_k}^*,$$

$$G = N_\infty = M_\infty, \qquad G^* = N_\infty{}^* = M_\infty{}^*.$$

It also follows from Theorem 3 and Corollary 4 that it is always possible to take subsets $\{N_{k_i}\}$ and $\{M_{k_i}\}$ of the sets $\{N_k\}$ and $\{M_k\}$ for which

$$M_{k_1} \subset M_{k_2} \subset \cdots \subset M_{k_i} \subset \cdots,$$

$$N_{k_1} \subset N_{k_2} \subset \cdots \subset N_{k_i} \subset \cdots.$$

and to exhibit a finite number m such that

$$N_k \subset M_{k+m} \qquad (k = 0, 1, 2, \ldots).$$

It should be noted that the sets G and G^* might have been defined as follows:

$$G = \bigcup_{k=0}^{\infty} N_k = \bigcup_{k=0}^{\infty} M_k,$$

$$G^* = \bigcap_{k=0}^{\infty} (N_k^* + G_{P_k}^*) = \bigcap_{k=0}^{\infty} (M_k^* + G_{P_k}^*).$$

If we construct the sequences

$$G_n = \bigcup_{k=0}^{n} M_k, \qquad G_n^* = \bigcap_{k=0}^{n} (M_k^* + G_{P_k}^*),$$

then, obviously,

$$G_n \to G \quad \text{and} \quad G_n^* \to G^* \quad \text{as} \quad n \to \infty.$$

Therefore, the sequences G_n and G_n^* can be used for an approximate determination of the sets of regular and spectral points of the operator A.

4. Error Estimates

Suppose that $\Delta_n = x^* - x_n$, where x^* and x_n denote, respectively, the exact and approximate solutions of Eq. (1.1).

Then Δ_n satisfies the equation

$$\Delta_n = \lambda A \Delta_n + \lambda A Q \delta_n. \tag{1.53}$$

Indeed, Eq. (1.20) yields the following expression for x_n:

$$\begin{aligned} x_n &= f + \lambda A Q x_{n-1} + \lambda A P x_n \\ &= f + \lambda A Q x_{n-1} + \lambda A x_n - \lambda A Q x_n \\ &= f + \lambda A x_n - \lambda A Q \delta_n. \end{aligned} \tag{1.54}$$

To obtain (1.53) we need only subtract this value of x_n from

$$x^* = f + \lambda A x^*.$$

By applying the operator $(I - \lambda A)^{-1}$ to Eq. (1.53), we obtain

$$\Delta_n = \lambda (I - \lambda A)^{-1} A Q \delta_n. \tag{1.55}$$

On the basis of Eq. (1.47), if we use formulas (1.28) and (1.32), we obtain

$$\Delta_n = \{I + \Omega_\lambda(I - L_\lambda)^{-1}\}(I - \lambda AP)^{-1}\lambda AQ\delta_n$$
$$= \Omega_\lambda\{I + (I - L_\lambda)^{-1}L_\lambda\}Q\delta_n = \Omega_\lambda(I - L_\lambda)^{-1}Q\delta_n. \quad (1.56)$$

From Eq. (1.56), we obtain an estimate for Δ_n:

$$\|\Delta_n\|_E \leqslant \|\Omega_\lambda(I - L_\lambda)^{-1}\| \cdot \|Q\delta_n\|_E. \quad (1.57)$$

This estimate is not of practical interest. Therefore, we shall give below a somewhat overrated but more practical estimate for Δ_n obtained from (1.57) under the assumption that the sufficient condition for the convergence of the method is satisfied, that is, that $L(\lambda) < 1$:

$$\|\Delta_n\|_E \leqslant \frac{\Omega(\lambda)}{1 - L(\lambda)} \|Q\delta_n\|_E, \quad (1.58)$$

where

$$\Omega(\lambda) = \|\Omega_\lambda\|. \quad (1.59)$$

In the case of $P = 0$, inequality (1.58) provides the following estimate of the error for the method of successive approximations:

$$\|\Delta_n\|_E \leqslant \frac{\|\lambda A\|}{1 - \|\lambda A\|} \|\delta_n\|_E. \quad (1.58')$$

If we need to estimate Δ_n *a priori* without knowing δ_n (for $n > 1$), we may use the estimate

$$\|\Delta_n\|_E \leqslant \frac{C\Omega(\lambda)L^{n-1}(\lambda)}{1 - L(\lambda)}, \quad (1.60)$$

where

$$C = \|Q\delta_1\|_E \qquad (C_k = \|Q_k\delta_1\|_E).$$

To see the validity of this estimate, we first obtain the expression for $Q\delta_n$ from Eq. (1.33):

$$\delta_n = x_n - x_{n-1} = \Omega_\lambda L_\lambda^{n-2}f^* + \Omega_\lambda L_\lambda^{n-1}x_0 - \Omega_\lambda L_\lambda^{n-2}x_0$$
$$= \Omega_\lambda L_\lambda^{n-2}(f^* + L_\lambda x_0 - x_0)$$
$$= \Omega_\lambda L_\lambda^{n-2}Q(f^* + \Omega_\lambda x_0 - x_0)$$
$$= \Omega_\lambda L_\lambda^{n-2}Q\delta_1$$

[see formulas (1.22) and (1.32)] and hence

$$Q\delta_n = Q\Omega_\lambda L_\lambda^{n-2} Q\delta_1 = L_\lambda^{n-1} Q\delta_1 .$$

It follows that

$$\|Q\delta_n\|_E \leqslant L^{n-1}(\lambda)\|Q\delta_1\|_E . \tag{1.61}$$

By substituting (1.61) in (1.58), we obtain inequality (1.60).

If the operator Q commutes with the operators $(I - L_n)^{-1}$ and Ω_λ, we obtain the following estimates for Δ_n:

$$\|\Delta_n\|_E \leqslant \frac{L(\lambda)}{1 - L(\lambda)} \|\delta_n\|_E ,$$

$$\|\Delta_n\|_E \leqslant \frac{L^n(\lambda)}{1 - L(\lambda)} \|\delta_1\|_E .$$

Let us suppose that by some other means we have succeeded in obtaining an estimate for the norm of the inverse operator $(I - \lambda A)^{-1}$. In other words, suppose that

$$\|(I - \lambda A)^{-1}\| \leqslant C^*,$$

Then we can obtain the following estimate of the error:

$$\|\Delta_n\|_E \leqslant C^* \|\varepsilon_n\|_E . \tag{1.62}$$

This is true because, by using formulas (1.9) and (1.8), we obtain

$$\begin{aligned} \lambda A Q \delta_n &= \lambda A \delta_n - \lambda A P \delta_n = \lambda A x_n - \lambda A x_{n-1} - \lambda A \alpha_n \\ &= \lambda A x_n + f - x_n = \varepsilon_n , \end{aligned} \tag{1.63}$$

and, by substituting (1.63) in (1.55), we obtain

$$\Delta_n = (I - \lambda A)^{-1} \varepsilon_n , \tag{1.64}$$

from which the relationship (1.62) follows.

Sometimes, it is useful to employ the relative estimate of the error

$$I_n = \frac{\|\Delta_n\|_E}{\|x^*\|_E} \leqslant \frac{100 \|\Delta_n\|_E \%}{\|x_n\|_E - \|\Delta_n\|_E} \qquad (n \geqslant n_0). \tag{1.65}$$

This relationship holds because the identity $x_n \equiv x^* - \Delta_n$ for sufficiently large n implies that

$$\|x^*\|_E \geqslant \|x_n\|_E - \|\Delta_n\|_E,$$

since $\|x_n\|_E \to \|x^*\|_E$ and $\|\Delta_n\|_E \to 0$ as $n \to \infty$.

On the basis of formulas (1.1) and (1.20), we have

$$\begin{aligned}\Delta_n &= \lambda A\Delta_{n-1} - \lambda AP\delta_n \\ &= \lambda A\Delta_{n-1} - \lambda AP(x_n - x^* + x^* - x_{n-1}) \\ &= \lambda AQ\Delta_{n-1} + \lambda AP\Delta_n,\end{aligned}$$

so that

$$\Delta_n = (I - \lambda AP)^{-1}\lambda AQ\Delta_{n-1} = \Omega_\lambda\Delta_{n-1} = \Omega_\lambda Q\Delta_{n-1}. \quad (1.66)$$

From relation (1.66), it follows that

$$\Delta_n = \Omega_\lambda L_\lambda^{n-1}\Delta_0. \quad (1.67)$$

Let us now consider the case in which we take $x_0 = \theta$ as our zeroth approximation. In this case, Eq. (1.67) takes the form

$$\Delta_n = \Omega_\lambda L_\lambda^{n-1}x^* = \Omega_\lambda L_\lambda^{n-1}Qx^*,$$

so that

$$\|\Delta_n\|_E \leqslant \Omega(\lambda)L^{n-1}(\lambda)\|Qx^*\|_E. \quad (1.68)$$

Consequently, we obtain from (1.68) the following estimate for I_n:

$$I_n \leqslant \sigma\Omega(\lambda)L^{n-1}(\lambda) \qquad (0 \leqslant \sigma \leqslant 1). \quad (1.69)$$

5. The Case of a Hilbert Space

The entire exposition in the preceding sections remains valid for a Hilbert space H. However, because of the special properties of Hilbert spaces, we shall obtain new properties of the method that are characteristic only of Hilbert spaces.

In the present section, we shall examine Eq. (1.1) under the assumption that the operator A operates in a Hilbert space H, that $f \in H$ and that P is a self-adjoint operator.

THEOREM 4. *If the operator A is self-adjoint and λ is a real number, then the operator L_λ is also self-adjoint.*

Proof. The operator L_λ can be represented in the form

$$L_\lambda = \lambda QAQ + \lambda^2 QAP(I - \lambda PAP)^{-1} PAQ. \tag{1.70}$$

To show this, note that on the basis of formula (1.20), the nth approximation can be determined from the equation:

$$x_n = f + \lambda AQx_{n-1} + \lambda AP^2 x_n. \tag{1.71}$$

Let us solve this equation as follows:

$$Px_n = Pf + \lambda PAQx_{n-1} + \lambda PAP^2 x_n,$$

$$Px_n = (I - \lambda PAP)^{-1}\{Pf + \lambda PAQx_{n-1}\},$$

$$\begin{aligned} x_n = f &+ \lambda AQx_{n-1} + \lambda AP(I - \lambda PAP)^{-1} Pf \\ &+ \lambda^2 AP(I - \lambda PAP)^{-1} PAQx_{n-1}. \end{aligned} \tag{1.72}$$

Keeping (1.22) in mind, we see from (1.72) that

$$\Omega_\lambda = \lambda AQ + \lambda^2 AP(I - \lambda PAP)^{-1} PAQ.$$

Since $L_\lambda = Q\Omega_\lambda$, the relation (1.70) follows.

The operators P, Q, and A are self-adjoint. Consequently, the operators PAP and $(I - \lambda PAP)^{-1}$ (where λ is a real number) are also self-adjoint.

From this fact, it is easy to establish the self-adjoint nature of the operator L_λ:

$$\begin{aligned} (L_\lambda f, g) &= \lambda(QAQf, g) + \lambda^2(QAP(I - \lambda PAP)^{-1} PAQf, g) \\ &= \lambda(f, QAQg) + \lambda^2(f, QAP(I - \lambda PAP)^{-1} PAQg) \\ &= (f, L_\lambda g) \qquad (f, g \in H). \end{aligned}$$

THEOREM 5. *If the operator A is self-adjoint and λ is a real number, then*

$$\Lambda(\lambda) = L(\lambda),$$

that is, the sufficient condition $L(\lambda) < 1$ for convergence of the method is also necessary.

Proof. On the basis of Theorem 4 and the hypothesis of the present theorem, the operator L_λ is self-adjoint. However, it is known that if the operator U is self-adjoint, then

$$\|U^n\| = \|U\|^n.$$

Consequently,

$$\Lambda(\lambda) = \lim_{n\to\infty} \sqrt[n]{\|L_\lambda{}^n\|} = \lim_{n\to\infty} \sqrt[n]{\|L_\lambda\|^n} = \|L_\lambda\| = L(\lambda).$$

In Section 2, we gave the sufficient condition $L_k(\lambda) < 1$ and also the necessary and sufficient condition (1.35) for convergence of the sequence

$$x_n = f + \lambda A x_{n-1} + \lambda A \alpha_n \tag{1.73}$$

to the solution of (1.1), where

$$\alpha_n = P_k \delta_n,$$

and P_k is a projection operator projecting the space H onto its finite-dimensional subspace $\tilde{H}$ (of dimension k)

The question then arises as to whether the sequence (1.73) converges if we increase the number k. In other words, will the sequence

$$\bar{x}_n = f + \lambda A \bar{x}_{n-1} + \lambda A \bar{\alpha}_n, \tag{1.74}$$

converge, where

$$\bar{\alpha}_n = P_{k+m} \bar{\delta}_n \qquad (m = 1, 2, 3, \ldots),$$

and P_{k+m} is a projection operator projecting the space H onto its finite-dimensional subspace $\tilde{H}$ (of dimension $k + m$)? Here, the projection operator P_{k+m} for arbitrary m can be represented in the form of a sum of two projection operators P_k and $P_m{}'$; that is, $P_{k+m} = P_k + P_m{}'$. Obviously, $P_k P_m{}' = P_m{}' P_k = 0$.

Examples show that in a Banach space convergence of the sequence (1.73) does not always imply convergence of the sequence (1.74). Actually, it is difficult to exhibit a class of operators in a Banach space for which such an implication is valid.

The matter is quite different in a Hilbert space H. In such a space, we can exhibit a class of operators (the self-adjoint operators) for which convergence of the sequence (1.73) does imply convergence of the sequence (1.74).

For a Hilbert space H, we have the following theorem:

THEOREM 6. *If* $L_k(\lambda) < 1$, *then, for arbitrary* m, *the sequence* (1.74) *converges to a solution of Eq.* (1.1) *and we have the following estimate of the error:*

$$\|\Delta_n\|_H \leqslant \frac{\Omega_k(\lambda)}{1 - L_k(\lambda)} \|Q_{k+m}\bar{\delta}_n\|_H, \tag{1.75}$$

where

$$Q_{k+m} = I - P_{k+m}.$$

Proof. First, we shall establish inequality (1.75). If we apply the considerations expounded at the beginning of Section 4, we obtain

$$\Delta_n = \lambda(I - \lambda A)^{-1} A Q_{k+m}\bar{\delta}_n \tag{1.76}$$

[see formula (1.55)].

Since the series on the right-hand side of Eq. (1.47) converges when $L_k(\lambda) < 1$, by substituting in (1.76) the value of the operator $(I - \lambda A)^{-1}$ given by formula (1.47), we obtain

$$\Delta_n = \lambda\left\{I + \sum_{n=0}^{\infty} \Omega_{k\lambda} L_{k\lambda}^n\right\}(I - \lambda A P_k)^{-1} A Q_{k+m}\bar{\delta}_n.$$

Since $Q_k Q_{k+m} = Q_{k+m}$, we obtain by use of formula (1.28)

$$\lambda(I - \lambda A P_k)^{-1} A Q_{k+m} = \lambda(I - \lambda A P_k)^{-1} A Q_k Q_{k+m} = \Omega_{k\lambda} Q_{k+m}.$$

Consequently,

$$\Delta_n = \left\{I + \sum_{n=0}^{\infty} \Omega_{k\lambda} L_{k\lambda}^n\right\}\Omega_{k\lambda}\Omega_{k+m}\bar{\delta}_n = \sum_{n=0}^{\infty} \Omega_{k\lambda} L_{k\lambda}^n Q_{k+m}\bar{\delta}_n. \tag{1.77}$$

From Eq. (1.77), we obtain inequality (1.75).

Let us now show that

$$\|Q_{k+m}\bar{\delta}_n\|_H \to 0 \tag{1.78}$$

as $n \to \infty$ if $L_k(\lambda) < 1$. By means of the projection operators

P_k, P_m', Q_{k+m} (where $P_k + P_m' = P_{k+m}$) we can write the sequence (1.74) in the form

$$\bar{x}_n = f + \lambda A P_k \bar{x}_n + \lambda A P_m' \bar{x}_n + \lambda A Q_{k+m} \bar{x}_{n-1},$$

whence

$$\bar{\delta}_n = \lambda A P_k \bar{\delta}_n + \lambda A P_m' \bar{\delta}_n + \lambda A Q_{k+m} \bar{\delta}_{n-1},$$

$$\bar{\delta}_n = \lambda (I - \lambda A P_k)^{-1} \{A P_m' \bar{\delta}_n + A Q_{k+m} \bar{\delta}_{n-1}\},$$

$$Q_k \bar{\delta}_n = \lambda Q_k (I - \lambda A P_k)^{-1} \{A P_m' \bar{\delta}_n + A Q_{k+m} \bar{\delta}_{n-1}\}.$$

Since $Q_k P_m' = P_m'$ and $Q_k Q_{k+m} = Q_{k+m}$, we obtain by using formula (1.32)

$$\begin{aligned} \lambda Q_k (I - \lambda A P_k)^{-1} A P_m' &= \lambda Q_k (I - \lambda A P_k)^{-1} A Q_k P_m' \\ &= L_{k\lambda} P_m', \\ \lambda Q_k (I - \lambda A P_k)^{-1} A Q_{k+m} &= \lambda Q_k (I - \lambda A P_k)^{-1} A Q_k Q_{k+m} \\ &= L_{k\lambda} Q_{k+m}. \end{aligned}$$

Consequently, we finally obtain

$$Q_k \bar{\delta}_n = L_{k\lambda} (P_m' \bar{\delta}_n + Q_{k+m} \bar{\delta}_{n-1}). \tag{1.79}$$

In view of the fact that the relationship

$$\|Q_k \bar{\delta}_n\|_H^2 = \|Q_{k+m} \bar{\delta}_n + P_m' \bar{\delta}_n\|_H^2 = \|Q_{k+m} \bar{\delta}_n\|_H^2 + \|P_m' \bar{\delta}_n\|_H^2,$$

is valid in the space H, we obtain from (1.79)

$$\begin{aligned} \|Q_{k+m} \bar{\delta}_n\|_H^2 + \|P_m' \bar{\delta}_n\|_H^2 &\leqslant \|L_{k\lambda}\|^2 \|P_m' \bar{\delta}_n + Q_{k+m} \bar{\delta}_{n-1}\|_H^2 \\ &\leqslant L_k^1(\lambda) \{\|P_m' \bar{\delta}_n\|_H^2 + \|Q_{k+m} \bar{\delta}_{n-1}\|_H^2\}, \end{aligned} \tag{1.80}$$

since

$$\begin{aligned} &|P_m' \bar{\delta}_n + Q_{k+m} \bar{\delta}_{n-1}\|_H^2 \\ &\quad = |(P_m' \bar{\delta}_n + Q_{k+m} \bar{\delta}_{n-1}, P_m' \bar{\delta}_n + Q_{k+m} \bar{\delta}_{n-1})| \\ &\quad = |(P_m' \bar{\delta}_n, P_m' \bar{\delta}_n) + (Q_{k+m} \bar{\delta}_{n-1}, P_m' \bar{\delta}_n) + (P_m' \bar{\delta}_n, Q_{k+m} \bar{\delta}_{n-1}) \\ &\qquad + (Q_{k+m} \bar{\delta}_{n-1}, Q_{k+m} \bar{\delta}_{n-1})| \\ &\quad = \|P_m' \bar{\delta}_n\|_H^2 + \|Q_{k+m} \bar{\delta}_{n-1}\|_H^2, \end{aligned}$$

$$(Q_{k+m} \bar{\delta}_{n-1}, P_m' \bar{\delta}_n) = (P_m' Q_{k+m} \bar{\delta}_{n-1}, \bar{\delta}_n) = 0.$$

From the hypothesis of the theorem, $L_k(\lambda) < 1$. Consequently, $L_k^2(\lambda) - 1 < 0$. Therefore, inequality (1.80) can be strengthened as follows:

$$\|Q_{k+m}\bar{\delta}_n\|_H \leqslant L_k(\lambda)\|Q_{k+m}\bar{\delta}_{n-1}\|_H \leqslant L_k^{n-1}(\lambda)\|Q_{k+m}\bar{\delta}_1\|_H, \quad (1.81)$$

from which (1.78) follows.

If we substitute (1.81) in (1.75), we obtain

$$\|\Delta_n\|_H \leqslant \frac{\Omega_k(\lambda)L_k^{n-1}(\lambda)}{1 - L_k(\lambda)} \|Q_{k+m}\delta_1\|_H. \quad (1.82)$$

It is clear from (1.82) that $\|\Delta_n\|_H \to 0$, as $n \to \infty$. This means that the sequence (1.74) converges to the solution of Eq. (1.1) for arbitrary m. This proves the theorem.

A consequence of Theorems 5 and 6 is the following:

THEOREM 7. *If the operator A is self-adjoint and λ is a real number, convergence of the sequence* (1.73) *always implies convergence of the sequence* (1.74); *that is,*

$$N_1 \subset N_2 \subset \cdots \subset N_k \subset \cdots.$$

Proof. Since $\lambda \in N_k$ for arbitrary $\Lambda_k(\lambda) < 1$ and (by virtue of Theorem 5) $\Lambda_k(\lambda) = L_k(\lambda)$, we have $L_k(\lambda) < 1$. Consequently, on the basis of Theorem 6, the sequence (1.74) converges for arbitrary m and $\lambda \in N_k$. Therefore, on the basis of Theorem 1, we have $\Lambda_{k+m}(\lambda) < 1$, that is, $\lambda \in N_{k+m}$, which is equivalent to the relation

$$N_k \subset N_{k+m} \qquad (k, m = 0, 1, 2, \ldots).$$

This last relation implies our theorem.

Theorems 6 and 7 are of practical value. The rapidity of convergence of the method depends on the smallness of $L_k(\lambda)$. For a given regular value λ, the quantity $L_k(\lambda)$ decreases with increasing k beginning with some $k \geqslant k_0$, as was shown earlier. However, calculation of $L_k(\lambda)$ is rather difficult for a sufficiently large k. In practice, we need to calculate $L_k(\lambda)$ until it becomes less than unity. However, $L_k(\lambda)$ may still be rather close to unity. For such values of k, the approximating process may converge very slowly. To increase the speed of convergence, we need to increase the number k, for example, by m units. It is clear from Theorems 6 and 7 that it is no longer necessary to calculate $L_{k+m}(\lambda)$ since we already know that the process will converge. Here, it is very convenient to use the estimate (1.75). For example, if $L_0(\lambda) < 1$ (for $\lambda_0 \in M_0$), that is, if the usual method of successive approximations converges, then, for arbitrary k and $\lambda \in M_0$, the Sokolov method converges.

Note. The estimate (1.75) remains valid for a Banach space. It is possible that Theorems 6 and 7 also hold for Banach spaces, but as yet this has not been proved. However, if we require not only that $L_k(\lambda)$ be less than unity, but also that the inequality

$$\|L_{k\lambda}Q_{k+m}\| + \|L_{k\lambda}P_m'\| < 1 \tag{1.83}$$

hold, then a sequence of the form (1.74) will converge.

Let us show this. From (1.79), we have

$$\|Q_k\bar{\delta}_n\|_E \leqslant \|L_{k\lambda}P_m'\| \; \|Q_k\bar{\delta}_n\|_E + \|L_{k\lambda}Q_{k+m}\| \; \|Q_{k+m}\bar{\delta}_{n-1}\|_E,$$

so that

$$\|Q_{k+m}\bar{\delta}_n\|_E \leqslant \|Q_k\bar{\delta}_n\|_E \leqslant \frac{\|L_{k\lambda}Q_{k+m}\|}{1 - \|L_{k\lambda}P_m'\|} \; \|Q_{k+m}\bar{\delta}_{n-1}\|_E. \tag{1.84}$$

It follows from (1.75) on the basis of (1.83) and (1.84) that $\|\Delta_n\|_E \to 0$ as $n \to \infty$.

6. Another Form of the Algorithm

In this section, we shall study another algorithm of the method, which is a modified special case of the preceding algorithm.

The idea behind the algorithm consists in defining the nth approximation as follows:

$$x_n = w_1 + w_2 + \cdots + w_n. \tag{1.85}$$

We determine the elements w_s successively from the relationships

$$w_1 = f + \lambda A \alpha_1^*, \tag{1.86}$$

$$w_s = \lambda A(w_{s-1} + \alpha_s^*) \qquad (s = 2, 3, \dots, n), \tag{1.87}$$

where

$$\alpha_1^* = P w_1, \tag{1.88}$$

$$\alpha_s^* = P\delta_s^*, \qquad \delta_s^* = w_s - w_{s-1}. \tag{1.89}$$

Since the formulas (1.86)–(1.89) determine w_s for $s = 1, 2, \dots, n$, they also determine the nth approximation x_n.

Let us show that the sequence (1.85) coincides with the sequence (1.33) if we set $x_0 = \theta$ in the latter sequence.

On the basis of formulas (1.86) and (1.88), we have

$$\alpha_1^* = Pf + \lambda P A \alpha_1^*,$$

so that

$$\alpha_1^* = (I - \lambda PA)^{-1} Pf. \tag{1.90}$$

Substituting (1.90) in (1.86) and using the notation of (1.27), we obtain

$$w_1 = f + \lambda A(I - \lambda PA)^{-1} Pf = f^*. \tag{1.91}$$

On the basis of formulas (1.87) and (1.89), we have

$$\delta_s^* = \lambda A w_{s-1} - w_{s-1} + \lambda A \alpha_s^*,$$

$$\alpha_s^* = \lambda PA w_{s-1} - P w_{s-1} + \lambda PA \alpha_s^*,$$

so that

$$\begin{aligned}\alpha_s^* &= (I - \lambda PA)^{-1}\{\lambda PA w_{s-1} - P w_{s-1}\}\\ &= (I - \lambda PA)^{-1} Q w_{s-1} - w_{s-1},\end{aligned} \tag{1.92}$$

since

$$\begin{aligned}(I - \lambda PA)^{-1}(\lambda PA - P) &= (I - \lambda PA)^{-1}(\lambda PA - I + I - P)\\ &= (I - \lambda PA)^{-1} Q - I.\end{aligned}$$

When we substitute (1.92) in (1.87), we obtain, in the notation of (1.28),

$$\begin{aligned}w_s &= \lambda A[w_{s-1} + (I - \lambda PA)^{-1} Q w_{s-1} - w_{s-1}]\\ &= \lambda A(I - \lambda PA)^{-1} Q w_{s-1} = \Omega_\lambda w_{s-1}.\end{aligned} \tag{1.93}$$

Consequently, on the basis of relations (1.91) and (1.93),

$$w_s = \Omega_\lambda L_\lambda^{s-2} f^*, \tag{1.94}$$

since

$$\Omega_\lambda \Omega_\lambda = \Omega_\lambda Q \Omega_\lambda = \Omega_\lambda L_\lambda .$$

If we now substitute (1.94) in (1.85), we finally obtain

$$x_n = (I + \Omega_\lambda + \Omega_\lambda L_\lambda + \cdots + \Omega_\lambda L_\lambda^{n-2}) f^*. \tag{1.95}$$

Equating the right-hand sides of formulas (1.33) and (1.95), we see that they coincide for $x_0 = \theta$. Thus, the condition for the convergence of the sequence (1.85) to the solution of the Eq. (1.1) is formulated in Theorem 1.

Formulas (1.57), (1.58), (1.60), (1.62), (1.65), and (1.69) are valid for estimating the error, except that in these formulas, we should have w_n instead of δ_n when this is necessary since, from formula (1.85), we have

$$\delta_n = x_n - x_{n-1} = w_n .$$

7. Comparison of the Methods of Sokolov and Galerkin

As we know, in the Galerkin method, the kth approximate solution is sought in the form

$$\bar{x}_k = \sum_{i=1}^{k} a_i \varphi_i . \tag{1.96}$$

The parameters a_i are determined from the conditions

$$f_i(P_k \bar{\varepsilon}_k) = 0 \qquad (i = 1, 2, \ldots, k), \tag{1.97}$$

where

$$\bar{\varepsilon}_k = f + \lambda A \bar{x}_k - \bar{x}_k , \tag{1.98}$$

P_k is a projection operator projecting the space E onto its finite-dimensional subspace $\tilde{E}$, $\{\varphi_i\}$ is a basis of the subspace $\tilde{E}$, and $\{f_i\}$ is a complete system of functionals defined on $\tilde{E}$.

If we substitute (1.96) in (1.98) and then substitute the result obtained in (1.97), we obtain a system of linear algebraic equations for determining the parameters a_i:

$$\sum_{i=1}^{k} \{f_i(\varphi_j) - \lambda f_i(P_k A\varphi_j)\} a_j = f_i(P_k f) \qquad (i = 1, 2, \ldots, k). \tag{1.99}$$

With the Sokolov method, we seek the first approximation in the form

$$x_1 = f + \lambda A \alpha_1 , \tag{1.100}$$

$$\alpha_1 = P_k x_1 = \sum_{i=1}^{k} c_i \varphi_i \qquad (x_0 = \theta). \tag{1.101}$$

Here the parameters c_i are determined, in accordance with (1.17), from the system of equations

$$f_i(\alpha_1 - \lambda P_k A \alpha_1) = f_i(P_k f) \qquad (i = 1, 2, \ldots, k). \tag{1.102}$$

When we substitute (1.101) in (1.102), we obtain a system of equations that coincides with the system (1.99). Consequently, $a_i = c_i$ and, obviously,

$$\bar{x}_k = P_k x_1 . \tag{1.103}$$

Equation (1.103) establishes a connection between the approximate solution obtained by the Galerkin method and the first approximation obtained by the Sokolov method.

By using the error estimates for the Sokolov method, we may obtain an error estimate for the Galerkin method. For example, the following error estimate is valid for the method of Galerkin:

$$\|\bar{\Delta}_k\|_E \leqslant \left\{1 + \frac{\Omega_k(\lambda)}{1 - L_k(\lambda)}\right\} \|\bar{\varepsilon}_k\|_E , \tag{1.104}$$

where $\bar{\Delta}_k = x^* - \bar{x}_k$ [cf. the notations of (1.59), (1.48), and (1.98)]. To see this, note that from the relationship

$$\bar{\Delta}_k = x^* - \bar{x}_k = x^* - x_1 + x_1 - \bar{x}_k = \Delta_1 + x_1 - \bar{x}_k$$

we have

$$\|\bar{\Delta}_k\|_E \leqslant \|\Delta_1\|_E + \|x_1 - \bar{x}_k\|_E . \tag{1.105}$$

On the basis of (1.100), (1.101), and (1.103), we obtain from (1.98)

$$\bar{\varepsilon}_k = f + \lambda A \alpha_1 - \bar{x}_k = x_1 - \bar{x}_k = x_1 - P_k x_1 = Q_k x_1 . \quad (1.106)$$

By using the error estimate (1.58) for $n = 1$ and $x_0 = \theta$, we finally have, on the basis of (1.105) and (1.106),

$$\|\bar{\Delta}_k\|_E \leqslant \frac{\Omega_k(\lambda)}{1 - L_k(\lambda)} \|Q_k x_1\|_E + \|Q_k x_1\|_E$$

$$= \left\{1 + \frac{\Omega_k(\lambda)}{1 - L_k(\lambda)}\right\} \|\bar{\varepsilon}_k\|_E .$$

In the case of a Hilbert space H, we may even use the estimate

$$\|\bar{\Delta}_k\|_H \leqslant \left\{1 + \frac{\Omega_m(\lambda)}{1 - L_m(\lambda)}\right\} \|\bar{\varepsilon}_k\|_H \qquad (0 \leqslant m \leqslant k). \quad (1.107)$$

8. The Connection between the Operators $\Omega_{k\lambda}$, $L_{k\lambda}$, $\Omega_{m\lambda}$, and $L_{m\lambda}$ $(m < k)$

Let us suppose that the projection operator P_k can be represented as a sum of two projection operators P_m and P_s'. In other words, suppose that

$$P_k = P_m + P_s', \quad Q_k = I - P_k, \quad Q_m = I - P_m \qquad (k = m + s).$$

Then,

$$\Omega_{k\lambda} = \Omega_{m\lambda}(I - P_s' L_{m\lambda})^{-1} Q_k , \quad (1.108)$$

$$L_{k\lambda} = Q_k L_{m\lambda}(I - P_s' L_{m\lambda})^{-1} Q_k . \quad (1.109)$$

To see this, note that we have, from Eq. (1.22),

$$\delta_n = \Omega_{k\lambda} \delta_{n-1} . \quad (1.110)$$

If we reason as we did in Section 5 for the relation (1.79), we obtain

$$\delta_n = \Omega_{m\lambda} P_s' \delta_n + \Omega_{m\lambda} Q_k \delta_{n-1} . \quad (1.111)$$

From Eq. (1.111), we evaluate $P_s'\delta_n$:

$$P_s'\delta_n = P_s'\Omega_{m\lambda}P_s'\delta_n + P_s'\Omega_{m\lambda}Q_k\delta_{n-1}$$
$$= P_s'L_{m\lambda}P_s'\delta_n + P_s'L_{m\lambda}Q_k\delta_{n-1},$$

since

$$P_s'\Omega_{m\lambda} = P_s'Q_m\Omega_{m\lambda} = P_s'L_{m\lambda},$$

$$P_s'\delta_n = (I - P_s'L_{m\lambda})^{-1}P_s'L_{m\lambda}Q_k\delta_{n-1}$$
$$= (I - P_s'L_{m\lambda})^{-1}(I - I + P_s'L_{m\lambda})Q_k\delta_{n-1}$$
$$= \{(I - P_s'L_{m\lambda})^{-1} - I\}Q_k\delta_{n-1}. \tag{1.112}$$

If we substitute (1.112) in (1.111), we get

$$\delta_n = \Omega_{m\lambda}(I - P_s'L_{m\lambda})^{-1}Q_k\delta_{n-1}. \tag{1.113}$$

On the basis of Eqs. (1.110) and (1.113), we obtain Eq. (1.108). Equation (1.109) can be obtained from Eq. (1.108) if we use the relation

$$L_{k\lambda} = Q_k\Omega_{k\lambda} = Q_kQ_m\Omega_{m\lambda} \qquad (Q_kQ_m = Q_k).$$

Let us assume that the projection operator P_k can be represented as a sum of projection operators P_{k_i}:

$$P_k = P_{k_1} + P_{k_2} + \cdots + P_{k_r}$$
$$(r \leqslant k; \qquad k_1 + k_2 + \cdots + k_r = k).$$

Then, we can start with the operators $\Omega_{0\lambda}$ and $L_{0\lambda}$ (where $\Omega_{0\lambda} = L_{0\lambda} = \lambda A$), and, with the aid of operator P_{k_1}, we can, on the basis of formulas (1.108) and (1.109), construct operators $\Omega_{k_1\lambda}$ and $L_{k_1\lambda}$, provided there exists an inverse operator $(I - P_{k_1}L_{0\lambda})^{-1}$. On the basis of these same formulas, we can start instead with operators $\Omega_{k_1\lambda}$ and $L_{k_1\lambda}$, and, with the aid of operator P_{k_2}, construct operators $\Omega_{k_2\lambda}$ and $L_{k_2\lambda}$ (where it is assumed that the inverse operator $(I - P_{k_2}L_{k_1\lambda})^{-1}$ exists). If we continue this process, then, after the rth step, we shall, as can be seen from formulas (1.108) and (1.109), obtain the operators $\Omega_{k\lambda}$ and $L_{k\lambda}$. This method makes it possible to construct the operators $\Omega_{k\lambda}$ and $L_{k\lambda}$ in practice.

9. Application of the Method to Equations that Can Be Reduced to Equations of the Form (1.1)

In the present section, we shall consider an equation of the form

$$Ax = g + \lambda Bx \tag{1.114}$$

under the assumption that the linear operators A and B are defined in a complex Banach space E_1 with range in a complex Banach space E_2. Here, λ is a complex parameter, g is a given element of the space E_2, and x is the unknown belonging to the space E_1. In addition, it is assumed that the operator A has a bounded inverse operator A^{-1}. If $B = I$ or $A = I$, we suppose the domain of definition and the range of the operator A or B to lie in the space E_2.

Under these assumptions, Eq. (1.114) can be written in the form

$$x = f + \lambda Ux, \tag{1.115}$$

where

$$f = A^{-1}g, \qquad U = A^{-1}B.$$

Let us solve Eq. (1.114) by the Sokolov method. As was stated earlier, the idea behind this method consists in determining the nth approximation from the equation

$$Ax_n = g + \lambda B(x_{n-1} + S^{-1}\alpha_n), \tag{1.116}$$

where

$$\alpha_n = PS\delta_n, \qquad \delta_n = x_n - x_{n-1} \qquad (n = 1, 2, 3, \ldots). \tag{1.117}$$

S is a linear operator mapping elements of the space E_1 into elements of a complex Banach space E_3 and possessing an inverse operator S^{-1}. In particular cases, the space E_3 may coincide with the space E_1 or E_2. P is a projection operator projecting the space E_3 onto its subspace $\tilde{E}_3$. As our zeroth approximation, we may take an arbitrary element x_0 in the space E_1.

On the basis of formulas (1.116) and (1.117), we obtain an equation for determining the element α_n:

$$x_n = f + \lambda U(x_{n-1} + S^{-1}\alpha_n), \tag{1.118}$$

$$\delta_n = \varepsilon_{n-1} + \lambda U S^{-1}\alpha_n,$$

$$\varepsilon_{n-1} = f - x_{n-1} + \lambda U x_{n-1},$$

$$\alpha_n = PS\varepsilon_{n-1} + \lambda PSUS^{-1}\alpha_n. \tag{1.119}$$

Instead of proceeding in the manner just described, we could reduce Eq. (1.114) to Eq. (1.115) and solve the latter by the Sokolov method. In either case, we would end up with the same sequence (1.118). Consequently, for this method it is unimportant whether we apply it directly to the given equation (1.114) or to its reduced form (1.115).

Let us set

$$Sx_n = v_n,$$

so that

$$x_n = S^{-1}v_n. \tag{1.120}$$

Then, Eqs. (1.118) and (1.117) take the form

$$v_n = Sf + \lambda SUS^{-1}(v_{n-1} + \alpha_n), \tag{1.121}$$

$$\alpha_n = P\delta_n^*, \qquad \delta_n^* = v_n - v_{n-1} \qquad (n = 1, 2, 3, \ldots). \tag{1.122}$$

We introduce the notations

$$p = Sf, \qquad U^* = SUS^{-1}. \tag{1.123}$$

Then, the sequence (1.121) is the nth approximation

$$v_n = p + \lambda U^*(v_{n-1} + \alpha_n), \qquad v_0 = Sx_0, \tag{1.124}$$

calculated by application of the Sokolov method to the equation

$$v = p + \lambda U^* v, \tag{1.125}$$

in which U^* is a linear operator operating in the space E_3 and $p \in E_3$.

Thus, convergence of the sequence (1.124) to the solution of Eq. (1.125) implies, by virtue of (1.120), convergence of the sequence (1.118) to the solution of Eq. (1.114). The convergence of the sequence (1.124) is studied in the second, third, and fifth sections of the present chapter.

Suppose that $\Delta_n^* = v^* - v_n$ and $\Delta_n = x^* - x_n$, where v^* and x^* are exact solutions of Eqs. (1.114) and (1.125) and v_n and x_n are approximate solutions of these equations. Then, in view of (1.120), we have the following relationship between Δ_n and Δ_n^*:

$$\Delta_n = S^{-1}\Delta_n^*. \tag{1.126}$$

If we use this relationship and also formulas (1.56) and (1.63), in which we replace A by $U^* = SUS^{-1} = SA^{-1}BS^{-1}$, we can obtain error estimates analogous to the error estimates (1.57), (1.58), (1.60), (1.62), and (1.65). For example, estimates exemplified by (1.58) and (1.65) are:

$$\|\Delta_n\|_{E_1} \leqslant \frac{\Omega^*(\lambda)}{1 - L^*(\lambda)} \|QS\delta_n\|_{E_3}, \tag{1.127}$$

$$I_n \leqslant \frac{100\|\Delta_n\|_{E_1}\%}{\|x_n\|_{E_1} - \|\Delta^n\|_{E_1}} \qquad (n \geqslant n_0), \tag{1.128}$$

where, from (1.28) and (1.32),

$$\Omega^*(\lambda) = \|\lambda A^{-1}BS^{-1}(I - \lambda PSA^{-1}BS^{-1})^{-1}Q\|, \tag{1.129}$$

$$L^*(\lambda) = \|\lambda QSA^{-1}BS^{-1}(I - \lambda PSA^{-1}BS^{-1})^{-1}Q\|. \tag{1.130}$$

By putting the operator S in different forms, we obtain variations of the algorithm for the Sokolov method. Let us consider some of these.

(1) $$S = I(E_3 = E_1).$$

According to (1.116) and (1.117), the approximations in this case are constructed from the formula

$$Ax_n = g + \lambda B(x_{n-1} + \alpha_n), \tag{1.131}$$

$$\alpha_n = P\delta_n \qquad (n = 1, 2, 3, \ldots), \tag{1.132}$$

so that

$$x_n = f + \lambda U(x_{n-1} + \alpha_n), \tag{1.133}$$

$$\alpha_n = P\varepsilon_{n-1} + \lambda PU\alpha_n. \tag{1.134}$$

The sequence (1.133) converges in norm in the space E_1 to the solution of Eq. (1.114) if, for example, the sufficient condition for convergence of the method

$$L^*(\lambda) = \|\lambda Q A^{-1} B (I - \lambda P A^{-1} B)^{-1} Q\| < 1$$

is satisfied.

(2) $$S = B(E_3 = E_2).$$

In this case, the approximations are constructed from the formula

$$A x_n = g + \lambda B x_{n-1} + \lambda \alpha_n, \tag{1.135}$$

$$\alpha_n = P B \delta_n \qquad (n = 1, 2, 3, \ldots). \tag{1.136}$$

On the basis of (1.135) and (1.136), we have

$$x_n = f + \lambda A^{-1} B x_{n-1} + \lambda A^{-1} \alpha_n, \tag{1.137}$$

$$\alpha_n = P B \varepsilon_{n-1} + \lambda P B A^{-1} \alpha_n. \tag{1.138}$$

A sufficient condition for convergence in norm in the space E_1 of the sequence (1.137) to the solution of Eq. (1.114) is of the form

$$L^*(\lambda) = \|\lambda Q B A^{-1} (I - \lambda P B A^{-1})^{-1} Q\| < 1.$$

This special case is studied in [40].

Note that in this case it is not necessary to assume existence of an inverse operator B^{-1}.

(3) $$S = A(E_3 = E_2).$$

The approximations are constructed from the formula

$$A x_n = g + \lambda B(x_{n-1} + \beta_n), \tag{1.139}$$

$$A\beta_n = \alpha_n, \qquad \alpha_n = P A \delta_n \qquad (n = 1, 2, 3, \ldots). \tag{1.140}$$

From (1.139) and (1.140), we have

$$x_n = f + \lambda A^{-1} B x_{n-1} + \lambda A^{-1} B A^{-1} \alpha_n, \tag{1.141}$$

$$\alpha_n = P A \varepsilon_{n-1} + \lambda P B A^{-1} \alpha_n. \tag{1.142}$$

From (1.138) and (1.142), it is clear that the equations for determining the element α_n in the second and third cases differ only in their free terms.

Note. All the above applies also to more general equations of the form

$$U_\lambda x = g \tag{1.143}$$

under the assumption that the linear operator U_λ, which depends on the complex parameter λ, is defined in a complex Banach space E_1 with range in a complex Banach space E_2 (that is, $g \in E_2$). The operator U_λ is defined for some set $\bar{G}$ of values of λ. In addition, it is assumed that the operator U_λ can be represented in the form

$$U_\lambda = A_\lambda + B_\lambda$$

in such a way that the operator A_λ has a bounded inverse A_λ^{-1} which is relatively easy to construct. Under these assumptions, Eq. (1.143) can be represented in one of the two forms

$$A_\lambda x = g - B_\lambda x,$$
$$x = A_\lambda^{-1} g - A_\lambda^{-1} B_\lambda x,$$

to which we can now apply the method just presented.

CHAPTER II

Application of the Method to Linear Integrodifferential Equations

1. Integral Equations in the Space $L^p(a, b)$

1. Let us consider the equation

$$y(x) = f(x) + \lambda \int_a^b K(x, \xi)\, y(\xi)\, d\xi, \tag{2.1}$$

with the assumptions (1) that the complex parameter λ is a regular value, (2) that the interval (a, b) is finite or infinite, and (3) that the complex-valued functions $f(x)$ and $K(x, \xi)$ of the real variables x and ξ satisfy the conditions

$$\left\{\int_a^b \left[\int_a^b |K(x, \xi)|^q\, d\xi\right]^{p/q} dx\right\}^{1/p} < \infty,$$

$$\left\{\int_a^b |f(x)|^p\, dx\right\}^{1/p} < \infty \qquad \left(\frac{1}{p} + \frac{1}{q} = 1\right), \tag{2.2}$$

$$\int_a^b |f(x)|\, dx < \infty, \qquad \int_a^b \operatorname*{vrai\,max}_{\xi} |K(x, \xi)|\, dx < \infty \tag{2.3}$$

$$(p = 1, \quad q = \infty),$$

$$\operatorname*{vrai\,max}_{x} |f(x)| < \infty, \qquad \operatorname*{vrai\,max}_{x} \int_a^b |K(x, \xi)|\, d\xi < \infty \tag{2.4}$$

$$(p = \infty, \quad q = 1).$$

Let us apply the Sokolov method to Eq. (2.1). In other words, we take as our nth approximation

$$y_n(x) = f(x) + \lambda \int_a^b K(x, \xi)[y_{n-1}(\xi) + \alpha_n(\xi)]\, d\xi, \qquad (2.5)$$

where

$$\alpha_n(x) = \int_a^b S_k(x, \xi)\, \delta_n(\xi)\, d\xi, \qquad (2.6)$$

$$\delta_n(x) = y_n(x) - y_{n-1}(x) \qquad (n = 1, 2, 3, \ldots), \qquad (2.7)$$

$y_0(x)$ is an arbitrary function in the space L^p, and $y_0(x)$ is an arbitrary function satisfying the conditions

$$S_k(x, \xi) = \int_a^b S_k(x, t) S_k(t, \xi)\, dt, \qquad (2.8)$$

$$\left\{\int_a^b \left[\int_a^b |S_k(x, \xi)|^q\, d\xi\right]^{p/q} d\xi\right\}^{1/p} < \infty, \qquad (2.9)$$

$$v(x) = \lim_{k\to\infty} \int_a^b S_k(x, \xi) v(\xi)\, d\xi, \qquad v(x) \in L^p. \qquad (2.10)$$

For example, the function

$$S_k(x, \xi) = \sum_{s=1}^{k} \mu_s \varphi_s(x) \overline{\psi_s(\xi)}$$

satisfies the conditions (2.8)–(2.10) if the sequences of functions $\{\varphi_s(x)\}$, $\varphi_s(x) \in L^p$ and $\{\psi_s(x)\}$, $\psi_s(x) \in L^q$ form a complete biorthogonal system and

$$\frac{1}{\mu_s} = \int_a^b \varphi_s(x) \overline{\psi_s(x)}\, dx.$$

On the basis of Eqs. (2.6) and (2.8), we write the nth approximation (2.5) in the form

$$y_n(x) = f(x) + \lambda \int_a^b K(x, \xi) y_{n-1}(\xi)\, d\xi + \lambda \int_a^b M_k(x, \xi) \alpha_n(\xi)\, d\xi, \qquad (2.11)$$

where

$$M_k(x, \xi) = \int_a^b K(x, t) S_k(t, \xi)\, dt. \qquad (2.12)$$

If we substitute (2.11) in (2.7) and then substitute the obtained result in (2.6), we get a linear integral equation for determining the function $\alpha_n(x)$:

$$\alpha_n(x) = g_{n-1}(x) + \lambda \int_a^b H_k(x, \xi)\alpha_n(\xi)\, d\xi, \tag{2.13}$$

$$H_k(x, \xi) = \int_a^b S_k(x, t)M_k(t, \xi)\, dt, \tag{2.14}$$

$$g_{n-1}(x) = \int_a^b S_k(x, \xi)\varepsilon_{n-1}(\xi)\, d\xi, \tag{2.15}$$

$$\varepsilon_{n-1}(x) = f(x) - y_{n-1}(x) + \lambda \int_a^b K(x, \xi)y_{n-1}(\xi)\, d\xi. \tag{2.16}$$

Let us suppose that λ is not an eigenvalue of the kernel $H_k(x, \xi)$. Then, from Eq. (2.13), we obtain

$$\alpha_n(x) = \int_a^b R_k(x, \xi, \lambda)g_{n-1}(\xi)\, d\xi, \tag{2.17}$$

where the function $R_k(x, \xi; \lambda)$ satisfies the equation

$$R_k(x, \xi, \lambda) = S_k(x, \xi) + \lambda \int_a^b H_k(x, t)R_k(t, \xi, \lambda)\, dt, \tag{2.18}$$

and

$$\begin{aligned} R_k(x, \xi, \lambda) &= \int_a^b S_k(x, t)R_k(t, \xi, \lambda)\, dt \\ &= \int_a^b R_k(x, t, \lambda)S_k(t, \xi)\, dt. \end{aligned} \tag{2.19}$$

If we substitute the value $\alpha_n(x)$ given by formula (2.17) into (2.11), we finally obtain the expression for the nth approximation.

2. Let us find a sufficient condition for convergence of the sequence (2.11) to the solution of Eq. (2.1).

On the basis of formulas (2.5) and (2.7), we have

$$\begin{aligned}\delta_n(x) &= \lambda \int_a^b K(x, \xi)\{\delta_{n-1}(\xi) - \alpha_{n-1}(\xi)\}\, d\xi \\ &\quad + \lambda \int_a^b K(x, \xi)\alpha_n(\xi)\, d\xi \\ &= \lambda \int_a^b \{K(x, \xi) - M_k(x, \xi)\}\{\delta_{n-1}(\xi) - \alpha_{n-1}(\xi)\}\, d\xi \\ &\quad + \lambda \int_a^b K(x, \xi)\alpha_n(\xi)\, d\xi, \end{aligned} \tag{2.20}$$

since, by virtue of (2.6), (2.8), and (2.12),

$$\begin{aligned}&\int_a^b M_k(x, \xi)\{\delta_{n-1}(\xi) - \alpha_{n-1}(\xi)\}\, d\xi \\ &\quad = \int_a^b\!\!\int_a^b K(x, t)S_k(t, \xi)\{\delta_{n-1}(\xi) - \alpha_{n-1}(\xi)\}\, dt\, d\xi \\ &\quad = \int_a^b K(x, t) \int_a^b S_k(t, \xi)\{\delta_{n-1}(\xi) - \alpha_{n-1}(\xi)\}\, d\xi\, dt = 0. \end{aligned} \tag{2.21}$$

Using (2.5) and noting (2.21), we can express the function $\varepsilon_{n-1}(x)$ in Eq. (2.16) in the form

$$\begin{aligned}\varepsilon_{n-1}(x) &= \lambda \int_a^b K(x, \xi)\{\delta_{n-1}(\xi) - \alpha_{n-1}(\xi)\}\, d\xi \\ &= \lambda \int_a^b \{K(x, \xi) - M_k(x, \xi)\}\{\delta_{n-1}(\xi) - \alpha_{n-1}(\xi)\}\, d\xi. \end{aligned} \tag{2.22}$$

If we substitute (2.22) in (2.15) and then substitute the result in (2.17), we obtain, in view of (2.19),

$$\begin{aligned}\alpha_n(x) = \lambda \int_a^b\!\!\int_a^b & R_k(x, t, \lambda)\{K(t, \xi) - M_k(t, \xi)\} \\ & \times \{\delta_{n-1}(\xi) - \alpha_{n-1}(\xi)\, dt\, d\xi. \end{aligned} \tag{2.23}$$

If we now substitute (2.23) in (2.20), we finally obtain

$$\delta_n(x) = \int_a^b \Omega_k(x, \xi, \lambda) z_{n-1}(\xi)\, d\xi, \tag{2.24}$$

where

$$z_n(x) = \delta_n(x) - \alpha_n(x), \tag{2.25}$$

$$\Omega_k(x, \xi, \lambda) = \lambda K(x, \xi) - \lambda M_k(x, \xi)$$
$$+ \lambda^2 \int_a^b \int_a^b K(x, \eta) R_k(\eta, t, \lambda)\{K(t, \xi) - M_k(t, \xi)\}\, d\xi\, d\eta. \tag{2.26}$$

The function $\Omega_k(x, \xi, \lambda)$ satisfies the equation [see (1.29)]

$$\Phi_k(x, \xi, \lambda) = \lambda K(x, \xi) - \lambda M_k(x, \xi) + \lambda \int_a^b M_k(x, t)\Omega_k(t, \xi, \lambda)\, dt. \tag{2.27}$$

If we substitute (2.24) in (2.6) and then substitute the result in (2.25), we obtain

$$z_n(x) = \int_a^b L_k(x, \xi, \lambda) z_{n-1}(\xi)\, d\xi, \tag{2.28}$$

where

$$L_k(x, \xi, \lambda) = \Omega_k(x, \xi, \lambda) - \int_a^b S_k(x, t)\Omega_k(t, \xi, \lambda)\, dt. \tag{2.29}$$

THEOREM 8. *If* $\bar{L}_k(\lambda) < 1$, *where*

$$\bar{L}_k(\lambda) = \left\{ \int_a^b \left[\int_a^b |L_k(x, \xi, \lambda)|^q\, d\xi \right]^{p/q} dx \right\}^{1/p}, \tag{2.30}$$

then the sequence (2.11) *converges in norm in the space* L^p *to the solution of Eq.* (2.1).

Proof. From the relations (2.24) and (2.28), we have

$$\left\{ \int_a^b |\delta_n(x)|^p\, dx \right\}^{1/p} \leqslant \bar{\Omega}_k(\lambda) \left\{ \int_a^b |z_{n-1}(\xi)|^p\, d\xi \right\}^{1/p}, \tag{2.31}$$

where

$$\bar{\Omega}_k(\lambda) = \left\{ \int_a^b \left[\int_a^b |\Omega_k(x, \xi, \lambda)|^q\, d\xi \right]^{p/q} dx \right\}^{1/p}. \tag{2.32}$$

$$\left\{ \int_a^b |z_n(x)|^p\, dx \right\}^{1/p} \leqslant \bar{L}_k(\lambda) \left\{ \int_a^b |z_{n-1}(\xi)|^p\, d\xi \right\}^{1/p}$$
$$\leqslant \bar{L}_k^{n-1}(\lambda) \left\{ \int_a^b |z_1(\xi)|^p\, d\xi \right\}^{1/p}. \tag{2.33}$$

Substituting (2.33) in (2.31), we obtain

$$\left\{\int_a^b |\delta_n(x)|^p\,dx\right\}^{1/p} \leqslant \bar{\Omega}_k(\lambda)\bar{L}_k^{n-2}(\lambda)\left\{\int_a^b |z_1(\xi)|^p\,d\xi\right\}^{1/p}.$$

Consequently, if $\bar{L}_k(\lambda) < 1$, then

$$\left\{\int_a^b |\delta_n(x)|^p\,dx\right\}^{1/p} \to 0, \quad \text{as} \quad n \to \infty.$$

Since the space L^p is complete, this implies the existence of the limit $y^*(x)$ of the sequence (2.11). Obviously, the function $y^*(x)$ is a solution of Eq. (2.1). This follows from relations (2.5) and (2.6).

THEOREM 9. *If conditions* (1)–(3) *are satisfied, then* $\bar{L}_k(\lambda) \to 0$ *as* $k \to \infty$.

The proof of this theorem is analogous to the proof of Theorem 3.

It follows from Theorem 9 that when these three conditions are satisfied, it is always possible to choose a function $S_k(x, \xi)$ such that $\bar{L}_k(\lambda) < 1$.

3. Suppose that

$$\Delta_n(x) = y^*(x) - y_n(x),$$

where $y^*(x)$ and $y_n(x)$ are the exact and approximate solutions of Eq. (2.1). Then, as in the discussion in Section 4 of Chapter I, we can obtain the following error estimates:

$$|\Delta_n(x)| \leqslant \frac{\varrho_n}{1 - \bar{L}_k(\lambda)}\,\bar{\Omega}_k(x, \lambda), \tag{2.34}$$

$$|\Delta_n(x)| \leqslant \frac{\varrho \bar{L}_k^{n-1}(\lambda)}{1 - \bar{L}_k(\lambda)}\,\bar{\Omega}_k(x, \lambda), \tag{2.35}$$

$$I_n(x) = \frac{|\Delta_n(x)|}{|y^*(x)|} \leqslant \frac{100|\Delta_n(x)|\,\%}{|y_n(x)| - |\Delta_n(x)|} \qquad (n \geqslant n_0), \tag{2.36}$$

$$I_n(x) \leqslant \theta\bar{\Omega}_k(x, \lambda)\bar{L}_k^{n-1}(\lambda) \tag{2.37}$$

$$(y_0(x) = 0; \qquad 0 \leqslant \theta \leqslant 1),$$

where

$$\overline{\Omega}_k(x, \lambda) = \left\{ \int_a^b |\Omega_k(x, \xi, \lambda)|^q \, d\xi \right\}^{1/q}, \tag{2.38}$$

$$\left\{ \int_a^b |\delta_n(x) - \alpha_n(x)|^p \, dx \right\}^{1/p}. \tag{2.39}$$

In addition to these estimates, we may also use the estimates (1.58), (1.60), (1.65), and (1.69), where, instead of $\Omega(\lambda)$, $L(\lambda)$, C, and $\|Q\delta_n\|_E$, we substitute, respectively, ϱ_1 and ϱ_n.

4. Suppose that $\{\varphi_i(x)\}$ and $\{\psi_i(x)\}$ are systems of linearly independent functions belonging, respectively, to the spaces L^p and L^q. Then, we shall determine the successive approximations from the relations

$$y_n(x) = f(x) + \lambda \int_a^b K(x, \xi)\{y_{n-1}(\xi) + \alpha_n(\xi)\} \, d\xi, \tag{2.40}$$

$$\alpha_n(x) = \sum_{i=1}^k c_{ni} \varphi_i(x), \tag{2.41}$$

where the coefficients c_{ni} are determined from the conditions

$$\begin{gathered} \int_a^b \{\alpha_n(x) - \delta_n(x)\}\overline{\psi_i(x)} \, dx = 0 \qquad (i = 1, 2, \ldots, k), \\ \delta_n(x) = y_n(x) - y_{n-1}(x) \qquad (n = 1, 2, 3, \ldots). \end{gathered} \tag{2.42}$$

If we substitute (2.41) in (2.42), we obtain a finite system of linear algebraic equations of the form

$$\begin{gathered} \sum_{j=1}^k \gamma_{ij} c_{nj} = \int_a^b \overline{\psi_i(x)} \, \delta_n(x) \, dx, \\ \gamma_{ij} = \int_a^b \varphi_j(x) \overline{\psi_i(x)} \, dx. \end{gathered} \tag{2.43}$$

We can determine the coefficients c_{nj} from the system (2.43) since the determinant of the system

$$c_{nj} = \sum_{i=1}^k \frac{D_{ij}}{D_k} \int_a^b \overline{\psi_i(x)} \, \delta_n(x) \, dx \tag{2.44}$$

is not zero; here

$$D_k = \begin{vmatrix} \gamma_{11} & \cdots & \gamma_{1k} \\ \cdot & \cdots & \cdot \\ \gamma_{k1} & \cdots & \gamma_{kk} \end{vmatrix},$$

and D_{ij} is the cofactor of the element v_{ij}. If we substitute (2.44) in (2.41), we obtain

$$\alpha_n(x) = \int_a^b S_k(x, \xi)\delta_n(\xi)\, d\xi,$$

where

$$S_k(x, \xi) = \sum_{i=1}^{k} \sum_{j=1}^{k} \frac{D_{ij}}{D_k} \varphi_j(x)\overline{\psi_i(\xi)}. \tag{2.45}$$

By carrying out certain simple transformations, we may show that the function $S_k(x, \xi)$ satisfies conditions (2.8)–(2.10). Consequently, the sequence (2.40) is a special case of the sequence (2.5).

When the systems of functions $\{\varphi_i(x)\}$ and $\{\psi_i(x)\}$ are biorthogonal and normalized, formulas (2.44) and (2.45) are simplified, taking the forms

$$c_{ni} = \int_a^b \overline{\psi_i(x)}\, \delta_n(x)\, dx, \tag{2.46}$$

$$S_k(x, \xi) = \sum_{i=1}^{k} \varphi_i(x)\, \overline{\psi_i(\xi)}. \tag{2.47}$$

Example 1. Let us consider the equation

$$y(x) = -20.2\sqrt{x} + 3 \int_0^1 \sqrt{x}(\xi + 10) y(\xi)\, d\xi, \tag{2.48}$$

which has the obvious solution $y(x) = \sqrt{x}$.

Let us solve Eq. (2.48) by the method we have explained. Suppose that $\varphi_1(x) = \psi_1(x) = 1$ and that $y_0(x) = 0$. Then, in accordance with (2.40) and (2.41), we take as our first approximation

$$\alpha_1(x) = c_1,$$

so that

$$y_1(x) = -20.2\sqrt{x} + \frac{63}{2} c_1 \sqrt{x}. \tag{2.49}$$

From (2.46), we have

$$c_1 = \int_0^1 y_1(x)\, dx. \tag{2.50}$$

Substituting (2.49) in (2.50), we obtain an equation for determining c_1:

$$c_1 = -\frac{202}{15} + 21c_1,$$

so that

$$c_1 = \frac{101}{150}.$$

Consequently, as our first approximation, we take

$$y_1(x) = 1.01\sqrt{x}.$$

From these same formulas [(2.40), (2.41), and (2.46)], we have as our second approximation

$$y_2(x) = -20.2\sqrt{x} + 3\int_0^1 \sqrt{x}(\xi + 10)\{y_1(\xi) + \alpha_2(\xi)\}\, d\xi,$$

$$\alpha_2(x) = c_2, \qquad c_2 = \int_0^1 \delta_2(x)\, dx,$$

$$y_2(x) = 1.212\sqrt{x} + \frac{63}{2}c_2\sqrt{x},$$

$$\delta_2(x) = 0.202\sqrt{x} + \frac{63}{2}c_2\sqrt{x},$$

$$c_2 = \frac{101}{750} + 21c_2,$$

$$c_2 = -\frac{101}{15000},$$

$$y_2(x) = 0.9999\sqrt{x}.$$

By continuing this process, we obtain as our nth approximation

$$y_n(x) = \sqrt{x} + (-1)^{n-1}\cdot 100^{-n}\sqrt{x}$$

$$y_1(x) = -20.2\sqrt{x} + 3\int_0^1 \sqrt{x}(\xi + 10)\alpha_1(\xi)\, d\xi.$$

For the present example, on the basis of (2.27), we have

$$\Omega_1(x, \xi, 3) = 3\sqrt{x}(\xi - \tfrac{1}{2}) + 3\int_0^1 \frac{21}{2}\sqrt{x}\,\Omega_1(t, \xi, 3)\,dt, \quad (2.51)$$

since $S_1(x, \xi) = 1$.

From (2.51) and (2.29), we have

$$\Omega_1(x, \xi, 3) = -\frac{3}{20}\sqrt{x}(\xi - \tfrac{1}{2}),$$

$$L_1(x, \xi, 3) = -\frac{3}{20}(\sqrt{x} - \tfrac{2}{3})(\xi - \tfrac{1}{2}).$$

Consequently, on the basis of (2.30) and (2.38) (for $p = q = 2$), we have

$$\bar{L}_1(3) = \frac{\sqrt{6}}{240}, \qquad \bar{\Omega}_1(x, 3) = \frac{\sqrt{3x}}{40}.$$

From formula (2.34), we have

$$|\Delta_n(x)| \leqslant 1.0413 \cdot 100^{-n}\sqrt{x}.$$

The exact value is

$$|\Delta_n(x)| = 100^{-n}\sqrt{x}.$$

From this we see that the difference between the estimated and exact values of $|\Delta_n(x)|$ amounts to 4.13 percent for all n and x.

The sufficient condition for convergence of the method of successive approximations usually employed is not satisfied in the present case since $\bar{L}_0^{\,2}(3) = 496.5 > 1$. Calculations show that in this example, the usual method of successive approximations diverges quite rapidly.

In general, for a given kernel, the method of successive approximations converges only for $|\lambda| < 15/106$, since $\lambda = 15/106$ is an eigenvalue. Sokolov's method converges for $\lambda < 15/106$ and for $\lambda > 15/106$.

5. For large values of k, formulas (2.30), (2.32), and (2.38) require lengthy computations. Therefore, we shall give some formulas which, while less exact, are more suitable for computations:

$$\tilde{L}_k(\lambda) = C_k(\lambda)\{1 + E_k(\lambda)\}, \tag{2.52}$$

$$C_k(\lambda) = \left\{\int_a^b \left[\int_a^b |\lambda K(x, \xi) - \lambda M_k(x, \xi)|^q \, d\xi\right]^{p/q} dx\right\}^{1/p},$$

$$E_k(\lambda) = \left\{\int_a^b \left[\int_a^b |R_k^*(x, \xi, \lambda)|^q \, d\xi\right]^{p/q} dx\right\}^{1/p},$$

$$R_k^*(x, t, \lambda) = \int_a^b \{M_k(x, \eta) - H_k(x, \eta)\} R_k(\eta, t, \lambda) \, d\eta;$$

$$\tilde{\Omega}_k(\lambda) = C_k(\lambda)\{1 + E_k^*(\lambda)\}, \tag{2.53}$$

$$E_k^*(\lambda) = \left\{\int_a^b \left[\int_a^b |\bar{R}_k(\xi, t, \lambda)|^q \, dt\right]^{p/q} d\xi\right\}^{1/p},$$

$$\bar{R}_k(x, t, \lambda) = \int_a^b M_k(x, \eta) R_k(\eta, t, \lambda) \, d\eta;$$

$$\tilde{\Omega}_k(x, \lambda) = C_k(x, \lambda) + C_k(\lambda) E_k^*(x, \lambda), \tag{2.54}$$

$$C_k(x, \lambda) = \left\{\int_a^b |\lambda K(x, \xi) - \lambda M_k(x, \xi)|^q \, d\xi\right\}^{1/q},$$

$$E_k^*(x, \lambda) = \left\{\int_a^b |\bar{R}_k(x, t, \lambda)|^q \, dt\right\}^{1/q}.$$

These formulas are obtained from formulas (2.30), (2.32), and (2.38) when we apply Hölder's and Minkowski's inequalities to them.

Example 2. The integral equation

$$y(x) = \sqrt{x} - 0.1(x^2 + 4x + 6) + \frac{1}{20}\int_0^1 (2x^2 + 15x^2 + 37x + 30)\xi^{x+1} y(\xi) \, d\xi \tag{2.55}$$

has the exact solution $y(x) = \sqrt{x}$.

For this equation, conditions (2.2) are satisfied for $p = q = 2$, and, on the basis of formulas (2.52),

$$\tilde{L}_2(1/20) = 0.1632.$$

$$S_2(x, \xi) = 1 + 3(2x - 1)(2\xi - 1).$$

Consequently, Sokolov's method converges. Since $\bar{L}_0^{\,2}(\lambda) \approx 1.8605 > 1$, we can say nothing definite with regard to the convergence of the method of successive approximations.

Suppose that

$$y_0(x) = 0, \qquad \varphi_1(x) = \psi_1(x) = 1,$$
$$\varphi_2(x) = \psi_2(x) = \sqrt{3}(2x - 1).$$

Then, on the basis of (2.40), (2.41), and (2.46), we have as our first approximation

$$y_1(x) = \sqrt{x} - 0.1(x^2 + 5x + 6) + \frac{1}{20}\int_0^1 (2x^3 + 15x^2 + 37x + 30)\xi^{x+1}\alpha_1(\xi)\, d\xi,$$

$$\alpha_1(x) = c_{11} + c_{12}\sqrt{3}(2x - 1),$$

$$c_{11} = \int_0^1 y_1(x)\, dx, \qquad c_{12} = \sqrt{3}\int_0^1 (2x - 1)y_1(x)\, dx, \quad (2.56)$$

$$y_1(x) = \sqrt{x} - 0.1(x^2 + 5x + 6) + \frac{c_{11}}{20}(2x^2 + 11x + 15) + \frac{c_{12}}{20}\sqrt{3}(2x^2 + 7x + 5). \quad (2.57)$$

If we substitute (2.57) in (2.56), we obtain the system of equations

$$7c_{11} + 55\sqrt{3}\,c_{12} = 26,$$
$$-13\sqrt{3}\,c_{11} + 93c_{12} = 4\sqrt{3},$$

from which we determine c_{11} and c_{12}:

$$c_{11} = 0.62877, \qquad c_{12} = 0.13090\sqrt{3}.$$

When we substitute these values of c_{11} and c_{12} in (2.57), we obtain as our first approximation

$$y_1(x) = \sqrt{x} + 0.00215x^2 - 0.01674x - 0.03026.$$

On the basis of these same formulas [(2.40), (2.41), and (2.46)], we get as our second approximation

$$y_2(x) = \sqrt{x} - 0.1(x^2 + 5x + 6)$$
$$+ \frac{1}{20}\int_0^1 (2x^3 + 15x^2 + 37x + 30)\xi^{x+1}$$
$$\times \{y_1(\xi) + \alpha_2(\xi)\}\, d\xi,$$
$$\alpha_2(x) = c_{21} + c_{22}\sqrt{3}(2x - 1),$$

$$c_{21} = \int_0^1 \delta_2(x)\, dx, \qquad c_{22} = \sqrt{3}\int_0^1 (2x - 1)\delta_2(x)\, dx, \quad (2.58)$$

$$y_1(x) = \sqrt{x} - 0.00448x^2 - 0.02342x - 0.03010 - \frac{0.00065}{x + 4}$$
$$+ \frac{c_{21}}{20}(2x^2 + 11x + 15) + \frac{c_{22}}{20}\sqrt{3}(2x^2 + 7x + 5),$$

$$\delta_2(x) = -0.00663x^2 - 0.00668x + 0.00016 - \frac{0.00065}{x + 4}. \quad (2.59)$$

On the basis of (2.58) and (2.59), we obtain the system of equations

$$7c_{21} + 55\sqrt{3}c_{22} = 0.66420,$$
$$-13\sqrt{3}c_{21} + 93c_{22} = -0.26556\sqrt{3},$$

from which we get

$$c_{21} = 0.037765, \qquad c_{22} = 0.002423\sqrt{3}.$$

Consequently, we have as our second approximation

$$y_2(x) = \sqrt{x} - \frac{0.00065}{x + 4} + 0.00002x^2 - 0.00011x + 0.00004.$$

Table I shows that the second approximation gives acceptable results.

Table II gives error estimates computed from formulas (1.58), (1.60), and (1.65), in which $L_k(\lambda)$ and $\Omega_k(\lambda)$ are replaced by $\tilde{L}_k(\lambda)$ and $\tilde{\Omega}_k(\lambda)$ [see formulas (2.52) and (2.53)]. This table also gives the exact values of Δ_n and I_n (here and in what follows, $\Delta_n = \|\Delta_n(x)\|$).

TABLE I

x	$y(x)$	$y_1(x)$	$y_2(x)$	$y(x) - y_1(x)$	$y(x) - y_2(x)$
0.00	0.00000	−0.03026	−0.00012	0.03026	0.00012
0.25	0.50000	0.46568	0.49986	0.03432	0.00014
0.50	0.70710	0.66901	0.70694	0.03809	0.00016
0.75	0.86604	0.82443	0.86584	0.04161	0.00017
1.00	1.00000	0.95515	0.99982	0.04485	0.00018

TABLE II

	Δ_n			I_n (percent)	
n	Exact value	Calculated from formula (1.58)	Calculated from formula (1.60)	Exact value	Calculated from formula (1.65)
1	0.03815	0.06575	0.06575	5.395	10.881
2	0.00015	0.00022	0.01073	0.022	0.032

From Table II, we can see that, from a practical point of view, the estimates for Δ_n and I_n obtained from formulas (1.58) and (1.65) are quite satisfactory. On the other hand, if we carry out the calculations with $\bar{L}_k(\lambda)$ and $\bar{\Omega}_k(\lambda)$, as determined from formulas (2.30) and (2.32), the estimates will be considerably more exact.

If we denote by $\bar{y}_k(x)$ the approximate solution calculated by the method of moments (replacing the kernel $K(x, \xi)$ by the degenerate kernel $M_k(x, \xi)$, which contains k terms), then the first approximation, as can be seen from (2.57), coincides with $y_2(x)$. Error estimates are given in [55] for

$$\Delta_k^* = \left\{\int_a^b |y^*(x) - \bar{y}_k(x)|^2 \, dx\right\}^{1/2},$$

that is,

$$\Delta_k^* \leqslant \frac{B^2 N}{1 - |\lambda| BN} \left\{\int_a^b |f(x)|^2 \, dx\right\}^{1/2}, \tag{2.60}$$

where

$$B = 1 + |\lambda| R_M, \qquad R_M = \left\{ \int_a^b \int_a^b |R_M(x, \xi, \lambda)|^2 \, d\xi \, dx \right\}^{1/2},$$

$R_M(x, \xi, \lambda)$ is the resolvent of the degenerate kernel $M_k(x, \xi)$, and

$$N = \left\{ \int_a^b \int_a^b |N_k(x, \xi)|^2 \, d\xi \, dx \right\}^{1/2},$$

$$K(x, \xi) = M_k(x, \xi) + N_k(x, \xi).$$

In the present example, it is not possible to estimate $\Delta_1 (\Delta_1 = \Delta_2{}^*)$ from Eq. (2.60) since $1 - |\lambda| BN \approx 1 - 1.7 < 0$. From formula (1.58) we get $\Delta_1 \leqslant 0.06575$, and we can see from Table II that this estimate for Δ_1 differs from the exact value by 73%.

With the method of moments, the accuracy of the approximate solution can be improved by increasing k, and with the Sokolov method it is improved by iterations. Let us find the approximate solution of Eq. (2.55) by using the method of moments for $k = 4$ and let us compare it with the approximate solution $y_2(x)$.

We have

$$\bar{y}_4(x) = \sqrt{x} - 0.1(x^2 + 5x + 6) + \frac{1}{20} \int_0^1 \sum_{i=1}^{4} K_i(x) \varphi_i(\xi) \bar{y}_4(\xi) \, d\xi, \tag{2.61}$$

where

$$\varphi_1(x) = 1, \qquad \varphi_2(x) = \sqrt{3}(2x - 1);$$

$$\varphi_3(x) = \sqrt{5}(6x^2 - 6x + 1),$$

$$\varphi_4(x) = \sqrt{7}(20x^3 - 30x^2 + 12x - 1),$$

$$K_1(x) = 2x^2 + 11x + 15,$$

$$K_2(x) = \sqrt{3}(2x^2 + 7x + 5),$$

$$K_3(x) = \sqrt{5}\left(2x^2 - x + 9 - \frac{36}{x + 4}\right),$$

$$K_4(x) = \sqrt{7}\left(2x^2 - 13x + 75 - \frac{600}{x + 5} + \frac{180}{x + 4}\right).$$

We seek a solution of Eq. (2.61) in the form

$$\bar{y}_4(x) = \sqrt{x} - 0.1(x^2 + 5x + 6) + \frac{1}{20}\sum_{i=1}^{4} \beta_i K_i(x),$$

where

$$\beta_i = \int_0^1 \varphi_i(x)\bar{y}_4(x)\,dx \qquad (i = 1, 2, 3, 4).$$

We obtain the following system for determining β_i:

$$0.05834\beta_1 + 0.45833\sqrt{3}\beta_2 + 0.06668\sqrt{5}\beta_3 - 0.00352\sqrt{7}\beta_4 = 0.21667,$$

$$-0.11090\sqrt{3}\beta_1 + 0.77500\beta_2 - 0.02326\sqrt{15}\beta_3 + 0.00021\sqrt{21}\beta_4 = 0.03333\sqrt{3}.$$

$$0.00333\sqrt{5}\beta_1 + 0.00333\sqrt{15}\beta_2 - 0.98657\beta_3 + 0.00061\sqrt{35}\beta_4 = 0.02238\sqrt{5},$$

$$-0.00004\sqrt{35}\beta_3 + 1.03650\beta_4 = 0.00635\sqrt{7},$$

from which we get

$$\beta_1 = 0.65822, \qquad \beta_2 = 0.13432\sqrt{3},$$

$$\beta_3 = -0.01907\sqrt{5}, \qquad \beta_4 = 0.00613\sqrt{7}.$$

Consequently,

$$\bar{y}_4(x) = \sqrt{x} + 0.00087x^2 - 0.02007x + 0.11241 + \frac{0.55782}{x+4} - \frac{1.28730}{x+5}.$$

By comparing the entries in the last two columns of Table III, we see that the second approximation in the Sokolov method is approximately forty-nine times as good as the result obtained by the method of moments for $k = 4$. It should be noted that more computation is involved in obtaining $\bar{y}_4(x)$ than in obtaining $y_2(x)$.

6. In Section 6 of Chapter I, we considered a second form of the algorithm. Let us apply it to Eq. (2.1). In other words, let us seek a solution in the form of a series

$$y(x) = \sum_{s=1}^{\infty} w_s(x).$$

We determine the functions $w_s(x)$ in succession from the relations

$$w_1(x) = f(x) + \lambda \int_a^b K(x, \xi)\beta_1(\xi)\, d\xi, \tag{2.62}$$

$$w_s(x) = \lambda \int_a^b K(x, \xi)[w_{s-1}(\xi) + \beta_s(\xi)]\, d\xi, \tag{2.63}$$

$$\beta_s(x) = \sum_{i=1}^{k} b_{si}\varphi_i(x) \qquad (s = 1, 2, 3, \ldots). \tag{2.64}$$

TABLE III

x	$y(x)$	$\bar{y}_4(x)$	$y(x) - \bar{y}_4(x)$	$y(x) - y_2(x)$
0.00	0.00000	−0.00559	0.00559	0.00012
0.25	0.50000	0.49349	0.00651	0.00014
0.50	0.70710	0.69959	0.00751	0.00016
0.75	0.86604	0.85744	0.00860	0.00017
1.00	1.00000	0.99021	0.00979	0.00018

We determine the coefficients b_{si} from the conditions

$$\int_a^b \{\beta_s(x) - \delta_s^*(x)\}\overline{\psi_i(x)}\, dx = 0 \qquad (i = 1, 2, \ldots, k), \tag{2.65}$$

where

$$\delta_s^*(x) = w_s(x) - w_{s-1}(x), \qquad w_0(x) = 0,$$

and $\{\varphi_i(x)\}$ and $\{\psi_i(x)\}$ are linearly independent systems of functions belonging to the spaces L^p and L^q, respectively.

When these systems of functions are biorthogonal, the coefficients b_{si} are determined from the equations

$$b_{si} = \frac{1}{\mu_i} \int_a^b \overline{\psi_i(x)\delta_s^*(x)}\, dx,$$

$$\mu_i = \int_a^b \varphi_i(x)\overline{\psi_i(x)}\, dx. \tag{2.66}$$

After successive determination of the first n functions $w_s(x)$, we take as our nth approximation

$$y_n(x) = \sum_{s=1}^{n} w_s(x). \tag{2.67}$$

If $\bar{L}_k(\lambda) < 1$, the sequence (2.67) converges in norm in the space L^p to the solution of Eq. (2.1) (see Section 6 of Chapter I).

To obtain error estimates we can make use of formulas (2.34)–(2.37) after replacing $\delta_n(x)$ in them by $w_n(x)$.

Example 3. Find the solution of the equation

$$y(x) = \exp\{-(23/4)x^2\} - \frac{2}{\sqrt{\pi}} \int_{-\infty}^{\infty} \exp\{-[11x^2 + (x-\xi)^2]/2\} y(\xi)\, d\xi.$$

Define

$$\varphi_1(x) = \psi_1(x) = \frac{1}{\sqrt[4]{\pi}} \exp\{-x^2/2\}.$$

Then, from (2.62), (2.64), and (2.66),

$$w_1(x) = \exp\{-23x^2/4\} - \frac{2}{\sqrt{\pi}} \int_{-\infty}^{\infty} \exp\{-[11x^2 + (x-\xi)^2]/2\} \beta_1(\xi)\, d\xi,$$

$$\beta_1(x) = \frac{b_1}{\sqrt[4]{\pi}} \exp\{-x^2/2\}, \qquad b_1 = \int_{-\infty}^{\infty} w_1(x) \frac{\exp\{-x^2/2\}}{\sqrt[4]{\pi}}\, dx,$$

so that

$$w_1(x) = \exp\{-x^2 23/4\}\left(1 - \frac{2b_1}{\sqrt[4]{\pi}}\right),$$

$$b_1 = \tfrac{2}{5}\sqrt[4]{\pi} - \tfrac{4}{5} b_1, \qquad b_1 = \tfrac{2}{9}\sqrt[4]{\pi}.$$

Thus,

$$y_1(x) = w_1(x) = \tfrac{5}{9}\exp\{-23x^2/4\}.$$

On the basis of (2.63), (2.64), and (2.66), we have

$$w_2(x) = -\frac{2}{\sqrt{\pi}}\int_{-\infty}^{\infty} \exp\{-[11x^2 + (x-\xi)^2]/2\}$$
$$\times [w_1(\xi) + \beta_2(\xi)]\, d\xi,$$

$$\beta_2(x) = \frac{b_2}{\sqrt[4]{\pi}}\, e^{-x^2/2}, \qquad b_2 = \int_{-\infty}^{\infty} \delta_2{}^*(x)\frac{e^{-x^2/2}}{\sqrt[4]{\pi}}\, dx,$$

from which we get

$$w_2(x) = -\tfrac{4}{9}e^{-5.96x^2} - \frac{2b_2}{\sqrt[4]{\pi}}\, e^{-23x^2/4},$$

$$\delta_2{}^*(x) = -\tfrac{5}{9}\, e^{-23x^2/4} - \tfrac{4}{9}\, e^{-5.96x^2} - \frac{2b_2}{\sqrt[4]{\pi}}\, e^{-23x^2/4},$$

$$b_2 = -0.39708\sqrt[4]{\pi} - \tfrac{4}{5}b_2, \qquad b_2 = -0.22060\sqrt[4]{\pi},$$

$$w_2(x) = 0.44120e^{-23x^2/4} - \tfrac{4}{9}\, e^{5.96x^2},$$

$$y_2(x) = 0.99676e^{-23x^2/4} - \tfrac{4}{9}\, e^{-5.96x^2}.$$

Analogously, for our third approximation, we obtain

$$y_3(x) = 0.99999e^{-23x^2/4} - 0.79741e^{-5.96x^2} + 0.34974e^{-5.9613x^2}.$$

In the present example, $\bar{L}_1(-1) = 0.16137$ and $\bar{\Omega}_1(-1) = 0.16236$. We cannot say whether the method of successive approximations converges or not since $\bar{L}_0(-1) = 1.0982 > 1$.

The exact solution is unknown. From formulas (1.58) and (1.65), we have

$$\Delta_1 \leqslant 0.052591, \qquad \Delta_2 \leqslant 0.000478, \qquad \Delta_3 \leqslant 0.000004,$$

$$I_1 \leqslant 15.07\,\%, \qquad I_2 \leqslant 0.16\,\%, \qquad I_3 \leqslant 0.0014\,\%,$$

$$y_1(0) = 0.55556, \quad y_2(0) = 0.55232, \quad y_3(0) = 0.55232.$$

7. What was just said applies also to equations of the form

$$u(P) = f(P) + \int_G K(P, Q, \lambda)u(Q)\, d\omega_Q,$$

where P and Q are points in some given bounded or unbounded region G of any number of dimensions or some surface or curve, and $d\omega_Q$ is an element of volume (area or arc length).

Let us pause to consider a special case of the construction of a system of functions $\{\varphi_i(P)\}$ and $\{\psi_i(P)\}$. Suppose that the region G is partitioned in some way into a finite number of subregions G_i:

$$G = \bigcup_{i=1}^{k} G_i .$$

On each of these subregions G_i, we define positive functions $\varrho_i(P)$ and $\mu_i(P)$, belonging, respectively, to the spaces L^p and L^q. Obviously,

$$\int_{G_i} \varrho_i(P)\mu_i(P)\, d\omega_P = c_i < \infty \qquad (i = 1, 2, \dots, k).$$

We construct the functions $\varphi_i(P)$ and $\psi_i(P)$ in the following way:

$$\varphi_i(P) = \begin{cases} \varrho_i(P), & P \in G_i, \\ 0, & P \bar{\in} G_i, \end{cases} \qquad \psi_i(P) = \begin{cases} \mu_i(P), & P \in G_i, \\ 0, & P \bar{\in} G_i . \end{cases}$$

These functions so constructed possess the property

$$\int_G \varphi_i(P)\psi_j(P)\, d\omega_P = \begin{cases} c_i \neq 0, & i = j, \\ 0, & i \neq j. \end{cases}$$

If some of the regions G_i are finite, it is simplest, from a practical point of view, to set $\varrho_i(P) = \mu_i(P) = 1$.

2. Integral Equations in the Space $L^2(a, b)$

In this section, we shall study certain properties of the method in connection with equations of the form (2.1) under the assumption that conditions (2.2) are satisfied for $p = q = 2$.

1. Consider the sequences

$$\bar{y}_n(x) = f(x) + \lambda \int_a^b K(x, \xi)[\bar{y}_{n-1}(\xi) + \bar{\alpha}_n(\xi)]\, d\xi, \quad (2.68)$$

$$y_n(x) = f(x) + \lambda \int_a^b K(x, \xi)[y_{n-1}(\xi) + \alpha_n(\xi)]\, d\xi, \quad (2.69)$$

where

$$\bar{\alpha}_n(x) = \int_a^b S_k(x, \xi)\bar{\delta}_n(\xi)\, d\xi,$$

$$\alpha_n(x) = \int_a^b S_{k+m}(x, \xi)\delta_n(\xi)\, d\xi,$$

$$S_{k+m}(x, \xi) = S_k(x, \xi) + S_m{}^*(x, \xi).$$

The functions $S_k(x, \xi)$ and $S_m{}^*(x, \xi)$ satisfy Eqs. (2.8)–(2.10) (for $p = q = 2$) and

$$\int_a S_k(x, t)S_m{}^*(t, \xi)\, dt = 0.$$

THEOREM 10. *If $\bar{L}_k(\lambda) < 1$ and the functions $S_k(x, \xi)$ and $S_m{}^*(x, \xi)$ are Hermitian symmetric, then, for an arbitrary choice of the function ($S_m{}^*(x, \xi)$, the sequence* (2.69) *converges to the solution of Eq.* (2.1) *and*

$$|\Delta_n(x)| \leqslant \frac{\bar{\Omega}_k(x, \lambda)}{1 - \bar{L}_k(\lambda)} \left\{ \int_a^b |\delta_n(x) - \alpha_n(x)|^2\, dx \right\}^{1/2}. \quad (2.70)$$

THEOREM 11. *If the functions*

$$K(x, \xi), \qquad S_k(x, \xi)uS_m{}^*(x, \xi)$$

are Hermitian symmetric, and λ is a real number, convergence of the sequence (2.68) *implies convergence of the sequence* (2.69) *to the solution of Eq.* (2.1).

The proofs of Theorems 10 and 11 are analogous to the proofs of Theorems 6 and 7.

It follows from Theorems 10 and 11 that:

(1) If the sufficient condition for the convergence of the method of approximations is satisfied (that is, if $\bar{L}_0(\lambda) < 1$), then the method of Sokolov converges for an arbitrary choice of the Hermitian symmetric function $S_m^*(x, \xi)$.

(2) If the kernel $K(x, \xi)$ is Hermitian symmetric and λ is a real number, then convergence of the method of successive approximations implies convergence of Sokolov's method for an arbitrary choice of the Hermitian symmetric function $S_m^*(x, \xi)$. Furthermore, the rapidity of convergence increases with increasing m.

Example 4. Consider the equation

$$y(x) = f(x) + \lambda \int_0^1 (1 - \sqrt{x})(1 - \sqrt{\xi})y(\xi)\, d\xi,$$

for which $\lambda = 6$ is an eigenvalue.

Suppose that

$$S_k(x, \xi) = \sum_{i=1}^{k} \varphi_i(x)\varphi_i(\xi),$$

where the $\varphi_i(x)$ are orthonormalized Legendre polynomials on [0, 1]. Then, from formula (2.29), we have for the given kernel

$$L_0(x, \xi, \lambda) = \lambda(1 - \sqrt{x})(1 - \sqrt{\xi}),$$

$$L_1(x, \xi, \lambda) = \frac{9\lambda}{9 - \lambda}\left(\tfrac{2}{3} - \sqrt{x}\right)\left(\tfrac{2}{3} - \sqrt{\xi}\right),$$

$$L_2(x, \xi, \lambda) = \frac{225\lambda}{225 - 37\lambda}\left(\sqrt{x} - \tfrac{4}{5}x - \tfrac{4}{15}\right)\left(\sqrt{\xi} - \tfrac{4}{5}\xi - \tfrac{4}{15}\right).$$

When we carry out the computations in accordance with formula (2.30), we obtain

$$\bar{L}_0^2(\lambda) = \frac{\lambda^2}{36}, \qquad \bar{L}_1^2(\lambda) = \frac{\lambda^2}{4(9 - \lambda)^2}, \qquad \bar{L}_2^2(\lambda) = \frac{\lambda^2}{4(225 - 37\lambda)^2}.$$

In the notations introduced in Section 2 of Chapter I, we have

$$M_0 = (-6, 6), \qquad M_1 = (-\infty, 6) + (18, \infty),$$

$$M_2 = (-\infty, 6) + (6\tfrac{12}{73}, \infty), \qquad M_0^* = (-\infty, -6] + [6, \infty),$$

$$M_1^* = [6, 18], \qquad M_2^* = [6, 6\tfrac{12}{73}].$$

In the present example, the sufficient condition for the convergence of the Sokolov method ($\bar{L}_k(\lambda) < 1$) is also a necessary condition. Consequently, the Sokolov method converges for $k = 1$ for all values of λ belonging to M_1 and, for $k = 2$, it converges for all $\lambda \in M_2$.

The method of successive approximations converges only for all $\lambda \in M_0$. If we compare the sets M_i $(i = 0, 1, 2)$, we see that the range of application of the Sokolov method is far wider than that of the method of successive approximations.

The function $y(x) = 2\sqrt{x}$ is a solution of the equation

$$y(x) = 5\sqrt{x} - 3 + 9\int_0^1 (1 - \sqrt{x})(1 - \sqrt{\xi})y(\xi)\, d\xi.$$

For $\lambda = 9$, we obtain

$$\bar{L}_0(9) = 1.5, \qquad \bar{L}_1(9) = \infty, \qquad \bar{L}_2(9) = \tfrac{1}{24}.$$

The method of successive approximations diverges.

For $k = 2$, the Sokolov method yields satisfactory convergence. If we carry out the calculations [taking $y_0(x) = 0$], we get our nth approximation

$$y_n(x) = 2\sqrt{x} + (-1)^n \cdot \frac{2}{24^n}(1 - \sqrt{x}).$$

On the basis of formula (2.34), we have

$$|\Delta_n(x)| \leqslant \frac{25}{23} \cdot \frac{2}{24^n}(1 - \sqrt{x}),$$

The exact value is

$$|\Delta_n(x)| = \frac{2}{24^n}(1 - \sqrt{x}).$$

The difference between the estimate and the exact value of $|\Delta_n(x)|$ does not exceed 8.7% for any value of n or x.

2. Depending on the specific choice of the function $S_k(x, \xi)$, we can obtain various forms of the algorithm. It was shown in the first section of the first chapter that if we take as our function $S_k(x, \xi)$ a function of the form (2.45), we obtain an algorithm characterized by formulas (2.40)–(2.42). We shall now give an algorithm that combines in a peculiar way the methods of successive approximations and least squares. The idea consists in determining the approximate solutions from the formulas

$$y_n(x) = f(x) + \lambda \int_a^b K(x, \xi)[y_{n-1}(\xi) + \alpha_n(\xi)]\, d\xi, \quad (2.71)$$

$$\alpha_n(x) = \sum_{i=1}^{k} c_{ni}\varphi_i(x), \quad (2.72)$$

where $\{\varphi_i(x)\}$ is an arbitrary system of linearly independent functions in the space L^2.

We shall determine the coefficients c_{ni} from the condition for the minimum of the functional

$$J(c_{n1}, \ldots, c_{nk}) = \int_a^b \{\alpha_n(x) - \delta_n(x)\}^2\, dx, \quad (2.73)$$

$$\delta_n(x) = y_n(x) - y_{n-1}(x) \qquad (n = 1, 2, 3, \ldots),$$

that is, from the conditions

$$\frac{\partial J}{2\partial c_{ni}} = 0 \qquad (i = 1, 2, \ldots, k). \quad (2.74)$$

(Here, we assume that $f(x)$ and $K(x, \xi)$ are real-valued functions.)

If we substitute (2.72) in (2.71) and then substitute the result in (2.73), we obtain on the basis of (2.74) the following system of linear algebraic equations for determining c_{ni}:

$$\sum_{j=1}^{k} a_{ij}c_{nj} = b_j \qquad (i = 1, 2, \ldots, k),$$

where

$$a_{ij} = \int_a^b K_i(x)K_j(x)\, dx,$$

$$K_i(x) = \varphi_i(x) - \lambda \int_a^b K(x, \xi)\varphi_i(\xi)\, d\xi,$$

$$b_i = \int_a^b \varepsilon_{n-1}(x)K_i(x)\, dx,$$

$$\varepsilon_{n-1}(x) = f(x) - y_{n-1}(x) + \lambda \int_a^b K(x, \xi)y_{n-1}(\xi)\, d\xi.$$

If we take $y_0(x) = 0$ as our zeroth approximation, the function $\alpha_1(x)$ will coincide with the approximate solution calculated by the method of least squares.

The algorithm (2.71)–(2.74) is a special case of the algorithm (2.5)–(2.7) for a particular choice of the function $S_k(x, \xi)$. Let us show that in the present case

$$S_k(x, \xi) = \sum_{i=1}^{k} \sum_{j=1}^{k} \frac{D_{ij}^*}{D_k^*} \varphi_j(x) K_i(\xi), \tag{2.75}$$

where

$$D_k^* = \begin{vmatrix} \beta_{11} & \cdots & \beta_{1k} \\ \cdot & \cdots & \cdot \\ \beta_{k1} & \cdots & \beta_{kk} \end{vmatrix},$$

$$\beta_{ij} = \int_a^b K_i(x)\varphi_j(x)\,dx,$$

and D_{ij}^* is the cofactor of the element β_{ij}.

From (2.73), we have

$$\int_a^b \{\alpha_n(x) - \delta_n(x)\} \frac{\partial}{\partial c_{ni}} \{\alpha_n(x) - \delta_n(x)\}\,dx = 0.$$

From (2.71) and (2.72), we have

$$\frac{\partial}{\partial c_{ni}} \{\alpha_n(x) - \delta_n(x)\} = \varphi_i(x) - \lambda \int_a^b K(x, \xi)\varphi_i(\xi)\,d\xi = K_i(x),$$

and, consequently,

$$\int_a^b \{\alpha_n(x) - \delta_n(x)\} K_i(x)\,dx = 0 \qquad (i = 1, 2, \ldots, k). \tag{2.76}$$

When we substitute (2.72) in (2.76), we obtain a system of linear algebraic equations

$$\sum_{j=1}^{k} \beta_{ij} c_{nj} = \int_a^b K_i(x)\delta_n(x)\,dx,$$

from which we obtain

$$c_{nj} = \sum_{i=1}^{k} \frac{D_{ij}^*}{D_k^*} \int_a^b K_i(x)\delta_n(x)\,dx. \tag{2.77}$$

If we substitute (2.77) in (2.72), then, by taking into account (2.75), we finally obtain

$$\alpha_n(x) = \int_a^b S_k(x, \xi)\delta_n(\xi)\, d\xi.$$

Example 5. Let us apply this algorithm to the equation

$$y(x) = (x-1)e^{-x} + 4\int_0^\infty e^{-x-\xi}y(\xi)\, d\xi,$$

Specifically, we take as our first approximation

$$y_1(x) = (x-1)e^{-x} + 4\int_0^\infty e^{-x-\xi}\alpha_1(\xi)\, d\xi,$$

$$\alpha_1(x) = c_1e^{-x/2},$$

so that

$$y_1(x) = (x-1)e^{-x} + \tfrac{8}{3}c_1e^{-x}.$$

In accordance with (2.73), we determine the coefficient c_1 from the condition for the minimum of the functional

$$\int_0^\infty \{\alpha_1(x) - y_1(x)\}^2\, dx$$

$$= \int_0^\infty \{c_1e^{-x/2} - \tfrac{8}{3}c_1e^{-x} - (x-1)e^{-x}\}^2\, dx.$$

From this, we obtain the following equation for determining the coefficient c_1:

$$\int_0^\infty \{c_1e^{-x/2} - \tfrac{8}{3}c_1e^{-x} - (x-1)e^{-x}\}(e^{-x/2} - \tfrac{8}{3}e^{-x})\, dx = 0.$$

After carrying out the calculations, we obtain $c_1 = 4/9$. Consequently,

$$y_1(x) = xe^{-x} + \tfrac{5}{27}e^{-x}.$$

For our second approximation, we take

$$y_2(x) = (x-1)e^{-x} + 4\int_0^\infty e^{-x-\xi}[y_1(\xi) + \alpha_2(\xi)]\, d\xi,$$

$$\alpha_2(x) = c_2e^{-x/2},$$

$$y_2(x) = xe^{-x} + \tfrac{10}{27}e^{-x} + \tfrac{8}{3}c_2e^{-x}.$$

We determine the coefficient c_2 from the condition

$$\int_0^\infty \{\alpha_2(x) - \delta_2(x)\}^2\,dx = \min,$$

$$\delta_2(x) = y_2(x) - y_1(x) = \tfrac{5}{27}e^{-x} + \tfrac{8}{3}c_2 e^{-x}.$$

That is, we have the following equation for determining c_2:

$$\int_0^\infty \{c_2 e^{-x/2} - \tfrac{8}{3}c_2 e^{-x} - \tfrac{5}{27}e^{-x}\}(e^{-x/2} - \tfrac{8}{3}e^{-x})\,dx = 0,$$

from which we obtain

$$c_2 = -\tfrac{10}{81}.$$

Thus,

$$y_2(x) = xe^{-x} + \tfrac{10}{243}e^{-x}.$$

By continuing this process, we obtain as our nth approximation

$$y_n(x) = xe^{-x} + \tfrac{5}{27}\cdot(\tfrac{2}{9})^{n-1}e^{-x}.$$

For the given kernel, $\lambda = 2$ is an eigenvalue. It follows that, in this case, the method of successive approximations results in a divergent process.

3. Integrodifferential Equations in the Space $L^p(a, b)$

1. Consider the equation

$$y(x) = f(x) + \lambda \int_a^b K(x, \xi)B[\xi, y(\xi)]\,d\xi, \tag{2.78}$$

where $B[x, y(x)]$ is a linear integrodifferential operator of finite order, $B[x, 0] \equiv 0$, λ is a complex parameter, and a and b are finite or infinite limits of integration.

Let us assume that

$$\int_a^b |f(x)|^p\,dx = C_1{}^p < \infty, \qquad \int_a^b\int_a^b |K(x, \xi)|^p\,d\xi\,dx = C_2{}^p < \infty, \tag{2.79}$$

$$\int_a^b \left\{\int_a^b |B[x, K(x, \xi)]|^p\,d\xi\right\}^{q/p} dx = C_3{}^q < \infty \qquad \left(\frac{1}{p} + \frac{1}{q} = 1\right).$$

For the case in which $p = 1$ and $q = \infty$, we have

$$\int_a^b |f(x)|\,dx = C_1 < \infty, \qquad \int_a^b\!\!\int_a^b |K(x, \xi)|\,d\xi\,dx = C_2 < \infty,$$

$$\operatorname*{vrai\,max}_x \int_a^b |B[x, K(x, \xi)]|\,d\xi = C_3{}^* < \infty.$$

When $p = \infty$ and $q = 1$, we have

$$\operatorname*{vrai\,max}_x |f(x)| = C_1{}^* < \infty, \qquad \operatorname*{vrai\,max}_{x,\xi} |K(x, \xi)| = C_2{}^* < \infty,$$

$$\int_a^b \operatorname{vrai\,max} |B[x, K(x, \xi)]|\,dx = C_3 < \infty.$$

Suppose that $\{\varphi_i(x)\}$ and $\{\psi_i(x)\}$ are systems of linearly independent functions belonging, respectively, to the spaces L^q and L^p. Then, by analogy with the method presented in Section 1 of Chapter II, we put for the nth approximation

$$y_n(x) = f(x) + \lambda \int_a^b K(x, \xi)\{B[\xi, y_{n-1}(\xi)] + \alpha_n(\xi)\}\,d\xi, \tag{2.80}$$

where

$$\alpha_n(x) = \sum_{i=1}^k c_{ni}\varphi_i(x) \qquad (n = 1, 2, 3, \ldots), \tag{2.81}$$

and $y_0(x)$ is an arbitrary function in the space L^p.

We determine the coefficients c_{ni} from the conditions

$$\int_a^b \{\alpha_n(x) - B[x, \delta_n(x)]\}\overline{\psi_i(x)}\,dx = 0 \tag{2.82}$$

$$(i = 1, 2, \ldots, k),$$

$$\delta_n(x) = y_n(x) - y_{n-1}(x). \tag{2.83}$$

In the case of the space L^2, the coefficients c_{ni} can also be determined from the condition for the minimum of the functional

$$\int_a^b \{\alpha_n(x) - B[x, \delta_n(x)]\}^2\,dx. \tag{2.82'}$$

If we substitute (2.80) in (2.83) and then substitute the result in (2.82), we obtain, in view of (2.81), a finite system of linear algebraic equations for the coefficients c_{ni}:

$$\sum_{j=1}^{k} (\gamma_{ij} - \lambda K_{ij})c_{nj} = b_{ni} \qquad (i = 1, 2, \ldots, k), \tag{2.84}$$

where

$$\gamma_{ij} = \int_a^b \varphi_j(x)\overline{\psi_i(x)}\, dx, \qquad K_{ij} = \int_a^b B[x, K_j(x)]\overline{\psi_i(x)}\, dx,$$

$$K_j(x) = \int_a^b K(x, \xi)\varphi_j(\xi)\, d\xi, \qquad b_{ni} = \int_a^b B[x, \varepsilon_{n-1}(x)]\overline{\psi_i(x)}\, dx,$$

$$\varepsilon_{n-1}(x) = f(x) - y_{n-1}(x) + \lambda \int_a^b K(x, \xi)B[\xi, y_{n-1}(\xi)]\, d\xi$$

$$= \lambda \int_a^b K(x, \xi)\{B[\xi, \delta_{n-1}(\xi)] - \alpha_{n-1}(\xi)\}\, d\xi.$$

We define

$$v_n(x) = B[x, y_n(x)].$$

Then, on the basis of (2.80) and (2.82),

$$v_n(x) = B[x, f(x)] + \lambda \int_a^b B[x, K(x, \xi)]\{v_{n-1}(\xi) + \alpha_n(\xi)\}\, d\xi, \tag{2.85}$$

$$\int_a^b \{\alpha_n(x) - \delta_n^*(x)\}\overline{\psi_i(x)}\, dx = 0 \qquad (i = 1, 2, \ldots, k), \tag{2.86}$$

$$\delta_n^*(x) = v_n(x) - v_{n-1}(x) \qquad (n = 1, 2, 3, \ldots).$$

Obviously, convergence in norm in L^q of the sequence (2.85) to the solution of the integral equation

$$v(x) = B[x, f(x)] + \lambda \int_a^b B[x, K(x, \xi)]v(\xi)\, d\xi$$

implies convergence in norm in L^p of the sequence (2.80) to the solution of Eq. (2.78).

On the basis of the results of Section 1 of the present chapter, the sufficient condition $L_k^*(\lambda) < 1$ ensures convergence of the sequence (2.80) to the solution of Eq. (2.78), where

$$L_k^*(\lambda) = \left\{\int_a^b \left[\int_a^b |L_k^*(x, \xi, \lambda)|^p \, d\xi\right]^{q/p} dx\right\}^{1/q}, \qquad (2.87)$$

$$L_k^*(x, \xi, \lambda) = B[x, \Omega_k^*(x, \xi, \lambda)] - \int_a^b S_k(x, t) B[t, \Omega_k^*(t, \xi, \lambda)] \, dt.$$

The function $S_k(x, \xi)$ is of the form (2.45), and the function $\Omega_k^*(x, \xi, \lambda)$ can be determined from the equation

$$\Omega_k^*(x, \xi; \lambda) = \lambda K(x, \xi) - \lambda M_k(x, \xi) + \lambda \int_a^b M_k(x, t) B[t, \Omega_k^*(t, \xi, \lambda)] \, dt, \qquad (2.88)$$

$$M_k(x, \xi) = \int_a^b K(x, t) S_k(t, \xi) \, dt.$$

Formulas of the form (2.34)–(2.36) are valid for error estimates if we replace $\bar{L}_k(\lambda)$, $\bar{\Omega}_k(x, \lambda)$ with $L_k^*(\lambda)$, $\Omega_k^*(x, \lambda)$ and ϱ_n^*, where

$$\Omega_k^*(x, \lambda) = \left\{\int_a^b |\Omega_k^*(x, \xi, \lambda)|^p \, d\xi\right\}^{1/p}, \qquad (2.89)$$

$$\varrho_n^* = \left\{\int_a^b |B[x, \delta_n(x)] - \alpha_n(x)|^q \, dx\right\}^{1/q}. \qquad (2.90)$$

Example 6. Consider the integral equation

$$y(x) = \sqrt{x} - \frac{x}{3} + \frac{x^3}{6} + \int_0^1 K(x, \xi) \sqrt{\xi}\, y(\xi) \, d\xi,$$

where

$$K(x, \xi) = \begin{cases} \frac{1}{2}(2 - \xi)x, & x \leqslant \xi, \\ \frac{1}{2}(2 - x)\xi, & x \geqslant \xi. \end{cases} \qquad [y(x) = \sqrt{x}].$$

In the above equation,

$$B[x, y(x)] = \sqrt{x}\, y(x),$$

and conditions (2.79) are satisfied for $p = q = 2$.

Suppose that

$$y_0(x) = \sqrt{x} - \frac{x}{3} + \frac{x^3}{6},$$

and

$$\varphi_1(x) = \psi_1(x) = 1.$$

Then, on the basis of (2.80) and (2.81), we take as our first approximation

$$y_1(x) = \sqrt{x} - \frac{x}{3} + \frac{x^3}{6} + \int_0^1 K(x, \xi)[\sqrt{\xi} y_0(\xi) + \alpha_1(\xi)]\, d\xi,$$

$$\alpha_1(x) = c_1,$$

so that

$$y_1(x) = \sqrt{x} - 0.06383x + 0.03810x^3\sqrt{x} - 0.00673x^5\sqrt{x} + c_1\left(\frac{3x}{4} - \frac{x^2}{2}\right).$$

On the basis of formula (2.82),

$$c_1 = \int_0^1 \sqrt{x}\delta_1(x)\, dx,$$

$$\delta_1(x) = y_1(x) - y_0(x) = \frac{x}{3} - \frac{x^3}{6} - 0.06383x + 0.03810x^3\sqrt{x} - 0.00673x^5\sqrt{x} + c_1\left(\frac{3x}{4} - \frac{x^2}{2}\right),$$

from which we get

$$c_1 = \tfrac{11}{70} c_1 + 0.07742, \qquad c_1 = 0.09186.$$

Consequently,

$$y_1(x) = \sqrt{x} + 0.03810x^3\sqrt{x} - 0.00673x^5\sqrt{x} - 0.04593x^2 + 0.00506x.$$

In an analogous manner, we obtain the following approximations:

$$y_2(x) = \sqrt{x} + 0.00012x^8 - 0.00127x^6 + 0.00291x^4\sqrt{x} - 0.00057x^3\sqrt{x} - 0.00209x^2 + 0.00032x.$$

$$y_3(x) = \sqrt{x} + 0.00002x^8\sqrt{x} - 0.00007x^7 + 0.00002x^6 + 0.00013x^4\sqrt{x} - 0.00004x^3\sqrt{x} - 0.00012x^2 + 0.00002x.$$

This equation can be solved by the method of successive approximations. The fifth approximation by this method is

$$\bar{y}_5(x) = \sqrt{x} - 0.00001x^6 + 0.00006x^3\sqrt{x} - 0.00010x.$$

If we solve the equation by Galerkin's method, that is, if we seek a solution of the form

$$y_k^*(x) = \alpha_1 + \alpha_2\sqrt{3}(2x-1) + \alpha_3\sqrt{5}(6x^2 - 6x + 1) + \cdots,$$

then, for $k = 3$, we obtain

$$y_3^*(x) = 0.17117 + 1.37316x - 0.57270x^2.$$

Table IV gives a comparison of the results obtained. In this example, on the basis of (2.87), (2.89), and (2.90), we have

$$L_1^*(1) = 0.06557, \qquad \varrho_1^* = 0.05642,$$

$$\Omega_1^{*2}(x, 1) = 0.03013x^5\sqrt{x} - 0.02009x^6\sqrt{x} + 0.09228x^5 - 0.31341x^4 + 0.22898x^3 + 0.00859x^2.$$

From a formula of the form (2.35), we obtain for an estimate of the error

$$|\Delta_1(x)| \leqslant 0.06038\Omega_1^*(x, 1), \qquad |\Delta_2(x)| \leqslant 0.00396\Omega_1^*(x, 1),$$

$$|\Delta_3(x)| \leqslant 0.00026\Omega_1^*(x, 1).$$

TABLE IV

x	$y(x)$	$y_1(x)$	$y_2(x)$	$y_3(x)$	$\bar{y}_5(x)$	$y_3^*(x)$
0.00	0.00000	0.00000	0.00000	0.00000	0.00000	0.17117
0.25	0.50000	0.49869	0.49995	0.50000	0.49998	0.47867
0.50	0.70710	0.70137	0.70680	0.70708	0.70706	0.71458
0.75	0.86604	0.85654	0.86548	0.86600	0.86598	0.87888
1.00	1.00000	0.99050	0.99942	0.99996	0.99995	0.97163

The difference between the estimate obtained and the exact value is shown in Table V.

TABLE V

x	$\|\Delta_1(x)\|$	Estimate $\|\Delta_1(x)\|$	$\|\Delta_2(x)\|$	Estimate $\|\Delta_2(x)\|$	$\|\Delta_3(x)\|$	Estimate $\|\Delta_3(x)\|$
0.00	0.00000	0.00000	0.00000	0.00000	0.00000	0.00000
0.25	0.00131	0.00330	0.00005	0.00022	0.00000	0.00001
0.50	0.00573	0.00727	0.00030	0.00048	0.00002	0.00003
0.75	0.00950	0.00997	0.00056	0.00065	0.00004	0.00004
1.00	0.00950	0.00983	0.00058	0.00064	0.00004	0.00004

If we were to carry out the calculations for estimating the error from a formula of the form (2.34), we would obtain more accurate results for the second and third approximations. For example,

$$|\Delta_3(x)| \leqslant 0.00022\Omega_1{}^*(x, 1).$$

Example 7. For the equation

$$y(x) = f(x) + \lambda \sqrt{\left(\frac{3}{2\pi}\right)} \int_{-\infty}^{\infty} x^2 \exp\{-(x^2 + 2\xi^2)/2\} y''(\xi)\, d\xi$$

$\lambda = 1.5$ is an eigenvalue.

If $f(x) \in L^2$, then for all nonnegative values of λ except 1.5, there is a unique solution. Let us see how much the range of applicability of the Sokolov method is broadened by increasing k.

We take as our orthonormal system of functions in $(-\infty, \infty)$ the weighted Chebychev-Hermite polynomials:

$$\varphi_m(x) = \psi_m(x) = \frac{H_{m-1}(x) e^{-x^2/2}}{\sqrt{[2^{m-1}(m-1)!\sqrt{\pi}]}}.$$

When $k = 0$, (2.80) and (2.81) lead to the method of successive approximations.

The sufficient condition $L_0^{*2}(\lambda) = 1.8876\, \lambda^2 < 1$ ensures convergence of this method in the interval $-0.7279 < \lambda < 0.7279$.

Because of (2.87), when $k = 1$ ($k = 2$), we have

$$L_1^{*2}(\lambda) = L_2^{*2}(\lambda) = 3.3970 \frac{\lambda^2}{(4-\lambda)^2}.$$

Consequently, the Sokolov method converges in the interval $-4.7444 < \lambda < 1.4069$.

When $k = 3$ ($k = 4$), we have

$$L_3^{*2}(\lambda) = L_4^{*2}(\lambda) = 1.1016 \frac{\lambda^2}{(12-7\lambda)^2}.$$

The range of applicability of the Sokolov method is extended to the entire interval of admissible values of λ outside the interval $1.4907 \leqslant \lambda \leqslant 2.0167$.

When $k = 5$, we have $L_5^{*2}(\lambda) = 0$ except at $\lambda = 1.5$. The method is applicable for any λ except the eigenvalue $\lambda = 1.5$. The second approximation gives the exact solution.

Suppose that $f(x) = e^{-x^2/2}$. Then, the equation

$$y(x) = e^{-x^2/2} - \sqrt{(3/2\pi)} \int_{-\infty}^{\infty} x^2 \exp\{-(x^2 + 2\xi^2)/2\} y''(\xi)\, d\xi$$

has the solution

$$y(x) = (1 + 0.4x^2)e^{-x^2/2}.$$

For $k = 3$, the first three approximations obtained by the Sokolov method are:

$$y_1(x) = (1 + 0.42105x^2)e^{-x^2/2},$$
$$y_2(x) = (1 + 0.39890x^2)e^{-x^2/2},$$
$$y_3(x) = (1 + 0.40006x^2)e^{-x^2/2}.$$

On the basis of formulas (2.87) and (2.89), we have for the present example

$$L_3^*(-1) = 0.05524, \qquad \Omega_3^*(x, -1) = \frac{0.04522}{\sqrt[4]{\pi}} x^2 e^{-x^2/2}.$$

If we carry out the calculations in accordance with a formula of the form (2.34), we obtain

$$|\Delta_1(x)| \leqslant 0.02468x^2e^{-x^2/2}, \qquad |\Delta_2(x)| \leqslant 0.00130x^2e^{-x^2/2},$$
$$|\Delta_3(x)| \leqslant 0.00007x^2e^{-x^2/2}.$$

The exact values are

$$|\Delta_1(x)| = 0.02105x^2e^{-x^2/2}, \qquad |\Delta_2(x)| = 0.00110x^2e^{-x^2/2},$$
$$|\Delta_3(x)| = 0.00006x^2e^{-x^2/2}.$$

Thus, the deviations from the exact value do not exceed 17.3, 18.2, and 16.7%, respectively.

The greatest values of $I_n(x)$ are:

$$I_1(\pm\infty) = 5.2625\,\%, \qquad I_2(\pm\infty) = 0.2750\,\%,$$
$$I_3(\pm\infty) = 0.0150\,\%.$$

Estimates of $I_n(x)$ obtained from a formula of the form (2.36) are:

$$I_1(\pm\infty) \leqslant 6.2265\,\%, \qquad I_2(\pm\infty) \leqslant 0.3270\,\%,$$
$$I_3(\pm\infty) \leqslant 0.0175\,\%.$$

2. The boundary-value problem for the integrodifferential equation

$$A[x, y(x)] + \lambda B[x, y(x)] = g(x), \tag{2.91}$$

$$U_s(y) = \sum_{j=0}^{m-1} [\bar{a}_{sj}y^{(j)}(a) + \bar{b}_{sj}y^{(j)}(b)] = 0 \tag{2.92}$$
$$(s = 0, 1, 2, \ldots, m-1),$$

where $A[x, y(x)]$ and $B[x, y(x)]$ are linear integrodifferential operators of orders m and r, respectively, with $m > r$, $A(x, 0) \equiv 0$, and $B(x, 0) \equiv 0$, can be reduced to an equation of the form (2.78). Here it is assumed that the Green's function $K(x, \xi)$ for the equation $A[x, y(x)] = 0$ under the conditions (2.92) exists and that it can be put in explicit form.

However, to get an approximate solution of the problem (2.91)–(2.92), we do not have to reduce it to an equation of the form (2.78). The method can be applied directly to the problem (2.91)–(2.92) by constructing successive approximations according to the formula

$$A[x, y_n(x)] + \lambda B[x, y_{n-1}(x)] + \lambda\alpha_n(x) = g(x), \tag{2.93}$$
$$U_s(y_n) = 0 \qquad (s = 0, 1, \ldots, m-1),$$

where

$$\alpha_n(x) = \sum_{i=1}^{k} c_{ni}\varphi_i(x). \tag{2.94}$$

Just as before, the coefficients c_{ni} are determined from the conditions (2.82). For the space L^2, they can also be determined from the condition for the minimum of the functional (2.82′).

Example 8. Find the solution of the equation

$$y''(x) + \frac{y(x)}{9x} + 24\int_0^1 y(\xi)\,d\xi = 19 - x,$$

$$y(0) = y(1) = 0 \qquad [y(x) = 9x - 9x^2].$$

In this equation,

$$A[x, y(x)] = y''(x), \qquad B[x, y(x)] = \frac{y(x)}{9x} + 24\int_0^1 y(\xi)\,d\xi.$$

Conditions (2.79) are satisfied for $p = q = 2$.

Suppose that $k = 1$ and that $\varphi_1(x) = \psi_1(x) = 1$. Then, from (2.87), $L_1^*(1) = 0.01944$. For $k = 0$, $L_0^*(1) = 2.235$. Consequently, we cannot say whether the method of successive approximations converges or not. Convergence of the Sokolov method is ensured and, what is more, it is rather rapid since $L_1^*(1)$ is small.

Let us take as our first approximation

$$y_1''(x) + \alpha_1 = 19 - x,$$

$$y_1(0) = y_1(1) = 0,$$

where

$$\alpha_1 = \int_0^1 B[x, y_1(x)]\,dx.$$

After some calculations, we obtain

$$y_1(x) = \frac{\alpha_1}{2}(x - x^2) - \frac{x^3}{6} + \frac{19}{2}x^2 - \frac{28}{3}x.$$

If we substitute $y_1(x)$ into the expression defining α_1 and make some simplifications, we obtain the equation

$$\frac{37}{36}\alpha_1 = 37\frac{167}{324},$$

so that $\alpha_1 = 36.5015$. Consequently,

$$y_1(x) = -\frac{x^3}{6} - 8.7507x^2 + 8.9174x.$$

For our second approximation, we put

$$y_2''(x) + \frac{y_1(x)}{9x} + 24\int_0^1 y_1(x)\,dx + \alpha_2 = 19 - x,$$

$$y_2(0) = y_2(1) = 0,$$

$$\alpha_2 = \int_0^1 B[x, \delta_2(x)]\,dx, \qquad \delta_2(x) = y_2(x) - y_1(x).$$

After some calculations, we obtain

$$y_2(x) = \frac{\alpha_2}{2}(x - x^2) + 0.0015x^4 - 0.0046x^3$$
$$- 8.9969x^2 + 9.0000x.$$

For determining α_2, we have the equation

$$\frac{37}{36}\alpha_2 = -0.00298,$$

so that $\alpha_2 = -0.0029$. Thus,

$$y_2(x) = 0.0015x^4 - 0.0046x^3 - 8.9954x^2 + 8.9985x.$$

TABLE VI

x	$y(x)$	$y_1(x)$	$y(x) - y_1(x)$	$y_2(x)$	$y(x) - y_2(x)$
0.2	1.4400	1.4322	0.0078	1.4399	0.0001
0.4	2.1600	2.1562	0.0038	2.1599	0.0001
0.5	2.2500	2.2501	−0.0001	2.2499	0.0001
0.6	2.1600	2.1642	−0.0042	2.1600	0.0000
0.8	1.4400	1.4482	−0.0082	1.4401	−0.0001

The maximum error for our first approximation does not exceed 0.55%. Consequently, the very first approximation gives a good result.

3. Let us stop for another algorithm of the method of solving problem (2.91)–(2.92) under the following hypotheses:

(1) The linear integrodifferential operators $A[x, y(x)]$ and $B[x, y(x)]$ map functions of the space L^q into functions of the space L^p, and $g(x) \in L^p$.

(2) The problem

$$A[x, w(x)] = 0, \tag{2.95}$$

$$U_s(w) = 0 \qquad (s = 0, 1, \ldots, m-1) \tag{2.96}$$

has only the trivial solution.

(3) The Green's function $G(x, \xi)$ for the problem (2.95)–(2.96) can be explicitly constructed.

Suppose that $\{\psi_i(x)\}$ is a system of linearly independent functions. We define functions $\varphi_i(x)$ from the problem

$$A[x, \varphi_i(x)] = \psi_i(x) \qquad (i = 1, 2, \ldots, k), \tag{2.97}$$

$$U_s(\varphi_i) = 0 \qquad (s = 0, 1, \ldots, m-1). \tag{2.98}$$

Then, we construct approximate solutions of the problem (2.91)–(2.92) from the formula

$$A[x, y_n(x)] + \lambda B[x, y_{n-1}(x) + \alpha_n(x)] = g(x), \tag{2.99}$$

$$U_s(y_n) = 0 \qquad (s = 0, 1, \ldots, m-1), \tag{2.100}$$

where

$$\alpha_n(x) = \sum_{i=1}^{k} c_{ni}\varphi_i(x). \tag{2.101}$$

We determine the zeroth approximation from the problem

$$A[x, y_0(x)] = v_0(x), \tag{2.99'}$$

$$U_s(v_0) = 0 \qquad (s = 0, 1, \ldots, m-1), \tag{2.100'}$$

where $v_0(x)$ is an arbitrary function in the space L^p. [In practice, we may set $v_0(x) = 0$ or $v_0(x) = g(x)$.]

We determine the coefficients c_{ni} from the conditions

$$\int_a^b A[x, \alpha_n(x) - \delta_n(x)]\overline{\varphi_i(x)}\, dx = 0 \qquad (i = 1, 2, \ldots, k),$$
$$\delta_n(x) = y_n(x) - y_{n-1}(x) \qquad (n = 1, 2, 3, \ldots). \tag{2.102}$$

In the case of the space L^2, the c_{ni} can be determined from the condition

$$\int_a^b \{A[x, \alpha_n(x) - \delta_n(x)]\}^2\, dx = \min. \tag{2.102'}$$

On the basis of (2.99),

$$A[x, \delta_n(x)] = \varepsilon_{n-1}(x) - \lambda B[x, \alpha_n(x)], \tag{2.103}$$
$$\varepsilon_{n-1}(x) = g(x) - A[x, y_{n-1}(x)] - \lambda B[x, y_{n-1}(x)].$$

If we substitute (2.103) in (2.102), we obtain a system of linear algebraic equations for determining c_{ni}. Once the c_{ni} are determined, we can determine the function $\alpha_n(x)$. If we now substitute the value of the function $\alpha_n(x)$ in (2.99) and solve the problem (2.99)–(2.100), we obtain the nth approximation $y_n(x)$.

We put

$$A[x, y_n(x)] = v_n(x), \tag{2.104}$$
$$U_s(y_n) = 0 \qquad (s = 0, 1, \ldots, m-1),$$

from which we obtain

$$y_n(x) = \int_a^b G(x, \xi) v_n(\xi)\, d\xi. \tag{2.105}$$

Then, by using (2.104) and (2.105), we can put the sequence (2.99) into the form

$$v_n(x) = g(x) + \lambda \int_a^b K(x, \xi)[v_{n-1}(\xi) + \alpha_n^*(\xi)]\, d\xi, \tag{2.106}$$

where

$$\alpha_n^*(x) = \sum_{i=1}^k c_{ni}\psi_i(x),$$
$$K(x, \xi) = -B[x, G(x, \xi)]. \tag{2.107}$$

Specifically, by virtue of (2.105) and (2.101) and the fact that the functions $\varphi_i(x)$ are determined from the problem (2.97)–(2.98), we have

$$\begin{aligned}
B[x, y_{n-1}(x) + \alpha_n(x)] &= B[x, y_{n-1}(x)] + B[x, \alpha_n(x)] \\
&= B\left[x, \int_a^b G(x, \xi)v_{n-1}(\xi)\, d\xi\right] \\
&\quad + B\left[x, \sum_{i=1}^k G_{ni} \int_a^b G(x, \xi)\psi_i(\xi)\, d\xi\right] \\
&= \int_a^b B[x, G(x, \xi)]v_{n-1}(\xi)\, d\xi \\
&\quad + \int_a^b B[x, G(x, \xi)] \sum_{i=1}^k c_{ni}\psi_i(\xi)\, d\xi \\
&= \int_a^b K(x, \xi)[v_{n-1}(\xi) + \alpha_n^*(\xi)]\, d\xi.
\end{aligned}$$

By means of analogous transformations, the conditions (2.102) for determining the coefficients c_{ni} can be put in the form

$$\int_a^b \{\alpha_n^*(x) - \delta_n^*(x)\}\overline{\varphi_i(x)}\, dx = 0,$$

$$\delta_n^*(x) = v_n(x) - v_{n-1}(x).$$

If we compare the sequences (2.40) and (2.106), we may conclude on the basis of the results of Section 1 of the present chapter that, if the functions $g(x)$ and $K(x, \xi)$ satisfy the conditions (2.2) and if $\bar{L}_k(\lambda) < 1$, then the sequence (2.106) must converge in norm in L^p to the solution of the integral equation

$$v(x) = g(x) + \lambda \int_a^b K(x, \xi)v(\xi)\, d\xi. \tag{2.108}$$

Suppose that $v^*(x)$ is the solution of Eq. (2.108). Then,

$$y^*(x) = \int_a^b G(x, \xi)v^*(\xi)\, d\xi \tag{2.109}$$

is the solution of the problem (2.91)–(2.92). To see this, note that we have from Eq. (2.109)

$$A[x, y^*(x)] = v^*(x). \tag{2.110}$$

When we substitute (2.110) in (2.108), we obtain

$$A[x, y^*(x)] = g(x) + \lambda \int_a^b K(x, \xi) v^*(\xi)\, d\xi.$$

Hence, because of (2.107) and (2.109),

$$\begin{aligned} A[x, y^*(x)] &= g(x) - \lambda \int_a^b B[x, G(x, \xi)] v^*(\xi)\, d\xi \\ &= g(x) - \lambda B[x, y^*(x)]. \end{aligned}$$

Consequently, the function $y^*(x)$ in (2.109) satisfies Eq. (2.91). It also satisfies conditions (2.92) since the function $G(x, \xi)$ satisfies these conditions.

Thus, convergence of the sequence (2.106) to the solution of Eq. (2.108) implies convergence of the sequence determined from the problem (2.99)–(2.100) to the solution of the problem (2.91)–(2.92).

In calculating $\bar{L}_k(\lambda)$ and $\bar{\Omega}_k(\lambda)$ from formulas (2.30) and (2.32), we must bear in mind that the kernel $K(x, \xi)$ has the form shown in (2.107) and that the function $S_k(x, \xi)$ has the form shown in (2.45), where we need only replace $\varphi_j(x)$ by $\psi_j(x)$, and $\psi_i(\xi)$ by $\varphi_i(\xi)$.

By a procedure analogous to that employed in Section 4 of Chapter I, we may, by considering (2.105), obtain the following estimates of the error:

$$|\Delta_n(x)| \leqslant \frac{\bar{\varrho}_n \bar{\Omega}_k(\lambda)}{1 - \bar{L}_k(\lambda)} \bar{G}(x), \tag{2.111}$$

$$|\Delta_n(x)| \leqslant \frac{\bar{\varrho}_1 \bar{\Omega}_k(\lambda) \bar{L}_k^{n-1}(\lambda)}{1 - \bar{L}_k(\lambda)} \bar{G}(x), \tag{2.112}$$

where

$$\bar{\varrho}_n = \left\{\int_a^b |A[x, \delta_n(x) - \alpha_n(x)]|^p \, dx\right\}^{1/p},$$

$$\bar{G}(x) = \left\{\int_a^b |G(x, \xi)|^q \, d\xi\right\}^{1/q},$$

$$\Delta_n(x) = y^*(x) - y_n(x).$$

Note 1. We can start with a sequence of approximate solutions $\{y_n(x)\}$ and form a new sequence of the form

$$z_n(x) = y_{n-1}(x) + \alpha_n(x) \qquad (n = 1, 2, 3, \ldots). \quad (2.113)$$

We can take the function $z_n(x)$ as the nth approximate solution of the problem (2.91)–(2.92) since

$$z_n(x) \to y^*(x) \qquad \text{as} \qquad n \to \infty$$

if the sequence $y_n(x)$ converges.

With such a construction of approximate solutions, the first approximation $z_1(x)$ coincides with the approximation obtained by the Galerkin method.

Example 9. Find the solution of the differential equation

$$y''(x) + (1 + x^2)y(x) + 1 = 0, \quad (2.114)$$

satisfying the boundary conditions

$$y(-1) = y(1) = 0.$$

In this example, we set

$$A[x, y(x)] = y''(x), \qquad B[x, y(x)] = (1 + x^2)y(x).$$

Suppose that $\psi(x) = -1$. Then, according to (2.97) and (2.98), the function $\varphi_1(x)$ should be determined from the problem

$$\varphi_1''(x) = -1,$$

$$\varphi_1(-1) = \varphi_1(1) = 0,$$

so that

$$\varphi_1(x) = \tfrac{1}{2}(1 - x^2).$$

On the basis of formulas (2.99), (2.100), and (2.101), our first approximation [with $y_0(x) = 0$] is determined from

$$y_1''(x) + (1 + x^2)\alpha_1(x) + 1 = 0, \tag{2.115}$$

$$y_1(-1) = y_1(1) = 0,$$

$$\alpha_1(x) = \frac{c_1}{2}(1 - x^2). \tag{2.116}$$

We determine the coefficient c_1 in accordance with (2.102) from the condition

$$\int_{-1}^{1} \{\alpha_1''(x) - y_1''(x)\}(1 - x^2)\, dx = 0. \tag{2.117}$$

If we substitute in (2.117) the value of $y_1''(x)$ given by (2.115) and the value of $\alpha_1(x)$ given by (2.116), we obtain the following equation for determining c_1:

$$\int_{-1}^{1} \left\{-c_1 + \frac{c_1}{2}(1 - x^4) + 1\right\}(1 - x^2)\, dx = 0,$$

that is,

$$\tfrac{19}{35} c_1 = 1,$$

so that $c_1 = 35/19$. Consequently,

$$\alpha_1(x) = \tfrac{35}{38}(1 - x^2).$$

Since the function $\alpha_1(x)$ is now determined, we find our first approximation from the problem

$$y_1''(x) + \tfrac{35}{38}(1 - x^4) + 1 = 0,$$

$$y_1(-1) = y_1(1) = 0,$$

from which we get

$$y_1(x) = \frac{1 - x^2}{2} + \frac{7}{228}(14 - 15x^2 + x^6),$$

$$y_1(x) = 0.92982 - 0.96052x^2 + 0.03070x^6.$$

As our second approximation, we obtain

$$y_2''(x) + (1 + x^2)\{y_1(x) + \alpha_2(x)\} + 1 = 0,$$
$$y_2(-1) = y_2(1) = 0,$$
$$\alpha_2(x) = \frac{c_2}{2}(1 - x^2), \tag{2.118}$$

that is,

$$y_2''(x) + \frac{c_2}{2}(1 - x^4) + \frac{1}{2}(1 - x^4) + 1$$
$$+ \tfrac{7}{228}(1 + x^2)(14 - 15x^2 + x^6) = 0,$$
$$y_2(-1) = y_2(1) = 0.$$

We determine the coefficient c_2 from the condition

$$\int_{-1}^{1} \{\alpha_2''(x) - \delta_2''(x)\}(1 - x^2)\, dx = 0, \tag{2.119}$$

$$\delta_2''(x) = \tfrac{8}{19}(1 - x^4) - \tfrac{7}{228}(1 + x^2)(14 - 15x^2 + x^6)$$
$$- \frac{c_2}{2}(1 - x^4). \tag{2.120}$$

When we substitute (2.118) and (2.120) in (2.119) and perform the calculations, we obtain the following equation for determining c_2:

$$\tfrac{19}{35} c_2 = \tfrac{12}{7315},$$

so that

$$c_2 = \tfrac{12}{3971} \approx 0.00302.$$

Consequently, we obtain the following equation for determining the second approximation $y_2(x)$:

$$y_2''(x) + 1 + 0.50151(1 - x^4)$$
$$+ \tfrac{7}{228}(1 + x^2)(14 - 15x^2 + x^6) = 0.$$

From this and the boundary conditions, we have

$$y_2(x) = 0.93193 - 0.96567x^2 + 0.00256x^4$$
$$+ 0.03207x^6 - 0.00055x^8 - 0.00034x^{10}.$$

In accordance with (2.113), we may also take the following functions as approximate solutions:

$$z_1(x) = \alpha_1(x) = \tfrac{35}{38}(1 - x^2),$$

$$z_2(x) = y_1(x) + \alpha_2(x) = 0.93133 - 0.96203x^2 + 0.03070x^6.$$

For comparison, we present a table of approximate solutions and of solutions found with a high degree of accuracy by numerical integration:

TABLE VII

x	$z_1(x)$	$y_1(x)$	$z_2(x)$	$y_2(x)$	$y(x$
0	0.92105	0.92982	0.93133	0.93193	0.93209
0.2	0.88421	0.89140	0.89285	0.89331	0.89345
0.4	0.77368	0.77626	0.77753	0.77762	0.77772
0.6	0.58948	0.58546	0.58643	0.58611	0.58616
0.8	0.33158	0.32314	0.32368	0.32323	0.32325
1	0	0	0	0	0

Note 2. The algorithm discussed in this paragraph can be applied without significant changes to finding the solutions of Eq. (2.91) that satisfy nonhomogeneous boundary conditions. In this case, the approximate solutions should be determined from the formulas

$$A[x, y_n(x)] + \lambda B[x, y_{n-1}(x) + \alpha_n(x)] = g(x), \quad (2.121)$$

where

$$U_s(y_n) = c_s^* \qquad (s = 0, 1, \ldots, m-1), \quad (2.122)$$

$$\alpha_n(x) = \sum_{i=1}^{k} c_{ni}\varphi_i(x).$$

The functions $\varphi_i(x)$ are determined from the problem (2.97)–(2.98) and the coefficients c_{ni} are determined from conditions (2.102) or from condition (2.102′). The zeroth approximation is determined from the problem

$$A[x, y_0(x)] = v_0(x) \qquad [v_0(x) \in L^p), \quad (2.121')$$

$$U_s(y_0) = c_s^* \qquad (s = 0, 1, \ldots, m-1). \quad (2.122')$$

The conditions for the convergence and the error estimates remain the same as in the case of homogeneous boundary conditions.

This remark applies also to the algorithm discussed in paragraph 2.

Example 10. Find the solution of the boundary-value problem

$$y''(x) - xy'(x) + \int_0^x \xi y(\xi)\, d\xi = 1,$$

$$y(0) = 1, \qquad y(1) + y'(1) = 0.$$

According to (2.121′) and (2.122′), the zeroth approximation is determined from the problem

$$y_0''(x) = 1,$$

$$y_0(0) = 1, \qquad y_0(1) + y_0'(1) = 0,$$

so that

$$y_0(x) = \frac{x^2}{2} - \frac{5}{4}x + 1.$$

Suppose that $\psi_1(x) = 1$. Then, in accordance with (2.97) and (2.98), we determine the function $\varphi_1(x)$ from the problem

$$\varphi_1''(x) = 1,$$

$$\varphi_1(0) = 0, \qquad \varphi_1(1) + \varphi_1'(1) = 0,$$

so that

$$\varphi_1(x) = \frac{x^2}{2} - \frac{3}{4}x.$$

On the basis of (2.121) and (2.122), we put for our first approximation

$$y_1''(x) - x[y_0'(x) + \alpha_1'(x)] + \int_0^x \xi[y_0(\xi) + \alpha_1(\xi)]\, d\xi = 1,$$

$$y_1(0) = 1, \qquad y_1(1) + y_1'(1) = 0,$$

$$\alpha_1(x) = c_1\left(\frac{x^2}{2} - \frac{3}{4}x\right). \tag{2.123}$$

After carrying out the calculations, we obtain

$$J_1''(x) = 1 - \frac{5}{4}x + \frac{x^2}{2} + \frac{5}{12}x^3 - \frac{x^4}{8}$$

$$+ c_1\left(x^2 - \frac{3}{4}x - \frac{x^4}{8} + \frac{x^3}{4}\right), \qquad (2.124)$$

$$y_1(0) = 1, \qquad y_1(1) + y_1'(1) = 0. \qquad (2.125)$$

We determine the coefficient c_1 from the condition

$$\int_0^1 \{\alpha_1''(x) - \delta_1''(x)\}\left(\frac{x^2}{2} - \frac{3}{4}x\right) dx = 0, \qquad (2.126)$$

$$\delta_1''(x) = y_1''(x) - y_0''(x) = c_1\left(x^2 - \frac{3}{4}x - \frac{x^4}{8} + \frac{x^3}{4}\right)$$

$$-\frac{5}{4}x + \frac{x^2}{2} + \frac{5}{12}x^3 - \frac{x^4}{8}. \qquad (2.127)$$

When we substitute (2.123) and (2.127) in (2.126), we obtain the following equation for determining c_1:

$$\int_0^1 c_1\left(1 + \frac{3}{4}x - x^2 - \frac{x^3}{4} + \frac{x^4}{8}\right)(2x^2 - 3x)\,dx$$

$$= \int_0^1 \left(-\frac{5}{4}x + \frac{x^2}{2} + \frac{5}{12}x^3 - \frac{x^4}{8}\right)(2x^2 - 3x)\,dx.$$

Therefore,

$$-\frac{275}{16\cdot 21}c_1 = \frac{1843}{16\cdot 21\cdot 15},$$

so that

$$c_1 = -\tfrac{1843}{4125} = -0.44677878\ldots.$$

If we now substitute this value of c_1 in (2.124) and solve the problem (2.124)–(2.125), we get as our first approximation

$$y_1(x) = 1 - 0.99379x + \frac{x^2}{2} - 0.15248x^3$$

$$+ 0.00443x^4 + 0.01525x^5 - 0.00231x^6.$$

The exact solution is $y(x) = e^{-x}$. The relative error for $x = 1$ does not exceed 0.9%.

Note 3. In the preceding sections, the coefficients were determined primarily by the methods of orthogonal projections and least squares. They can also be determined by the method of collocations, the method of subregions, the Ritz method, and in various other ways.

Let us construct the first two approximate solutions of Eq. (2.114) by the method of collocations for determining the coefficients c_1 and c_2.

We determine the first approximation from the problem

$$\begin{gathered} y_1''(x) + (1 + x^2)\alpha_1(x) + 1 = 0, \\ y_1(-1) = y_1(1) = 0, \end{gathered} \tag{2.128}$$

where the function $\alpha_1(x)$ has the form shown in (2.116).

We determine the coefficient c_1 from the condition

$$\alpha_1''(0) - y_1''(0) = 0.$$

On the basis of (2.116) and (2.128), we have

$$\alpha_1''(x) - y_1''(x) = -c_1 + \frac{c_1}{2}(1 - x^4) + 1.$$

Consequently, we can determine c_1 from the equation

$$-c_1 + \frac{c_1}{2} + 1 = 0,$$

so that $c_1 = 2$.

Thus,

$$\alpha_1(x) = 1 - x^2,$$

$$y_1(x) = \frac{1 - x^2}{2} + \frac{1}{30}(14 - 15x^2 + x^6).$$

We take as our second approximation

$$y_2''(x) + (1 + x^2)[y_1(x) + \alpha_2(x)] + 1 = 0,$$

$$\alpha_2(x) = \frac{c_2}{2}(1 - x^2),$$

that is, we determine the second approximation from the condition

$$y_2''(x) + \frac{c_2}{2}(1 - x^4) + \tfrac{1}{2}(1 - x^4)$$
$$+ \tfrac{1}{30}(1 + x^2)(14 - 15x^2 + x^6) + 1 = 0,$$
$$y_2(-1) = y_2(1) = 0.$$

We determine the coefficient c_2 from the condition

$$\alpha_2''(0) - \delta_2''(0) = 0,$$

$$\alpha_2''(x) - \delta_2''(x) = -c_2 + \frac{c_2}{2}(1 - x^4) - \tfrac{1}{2}(1 - x^2)$$
$$+ \tfrac{1}{30}(1 + x^2)(14 - 15x^2 + x^6),$$

$$-c_2 + \frac{c_2}{2} - \frac{1}{30} = 0, \qquad c_2 = -\tfrac{1}{15}.$$

Consequently,

$$\alpha_2(x) = -\tfrac{1}{30}(1 - x^2),$$

$$y_2(x) = \frac{1 - x^2}{2} + \frac{7}{450}(14 - 15x^2 + x^6)$$
$$+ \frac{1}{30}\left(\frac{16243}{2520} - 7x^2 + \frac{x^4}{12} + \frac{x^6}{2} - \frac{x^8}{56} - \frac{x^{10}}{90}\right).$$

In accordance with (2.113), as our first two approximations, we may take the functions

$$z_1(x) = \alpha_1(x) = 1 - x^2,$$

$$z_2(x) = y_1(x) + \alpha_2(x) = \tfrac{7}{15}(1 - x^2) + \tfrac{1}{30}(14 - 15x^2 + x^6),$$

$$z_1(0) = 1, \qquad y_1(0) = 0.96667,$$

$$z_2(0) = 0.93333, \qquad y_2(0) = 0.93263.$$

4. Comparison of the Method of Moments and the Sokolov Method

In the present section, we shall compare the method of moments as expounded in [7] with Sokolov's method in connection with the integral equation (2.1).

With the method of moments, we seek an approximate solution of the integral equation (2.1), in the form

$$y_k^*(x) = a_0 z_0(x) + a_1 z_1(x) + \cdots + a_{k-1} z_{k-1}(x), \quad (2.129)$$

where

$$t_0(x) = f(x), \qquad z_i(x) = \int_a^b K(x, \xi) z_{i-1}(\xi)\, d\xi, \quad (2.130)$$

and the coefficients a_i are determined from the following formulas:

$$a_0 = 1 - \frac{\alpha_0}{P_k(1/\lambda)}, \qquad a_i = \lambda a_{i-1} - \frac{\alpha_i^*}{P_k(1/\lambda)} \quad (i = 1, 2, \ldots, k-1), \quad (2.131)$$

$$P_k\left(\frac{1}{\lambda}\right) = \frac{1}{\lambda^k}(1 + \alpha_{k-1}^* \lambda + \cdots + \alpha_1 \lambda^{k-1} + \alpha_0 \lambda^k),$$

$$\sum_{j=0}^{k-1} (z_i, z_j)\alpha_j^* + (z_i, z_k) = 0 \qquad (i = 0, 1, \ldots, k-1), \quad (2.132)$$

$$(z_i, z_j) = \int_a^b z_i(x) z_j(x)\, dx.$$

If we determine the first approximation by the Sokolov method in the following manner:

$$y_1(x) = f(x) + \lambda \int_a^b K(x, \xi)\alpha_1(\xi)\, d\xi,$$

$$\alpha_1(x) = \sum_{i=1}^{k} c_{1i} z_{i-1}(x),$$

$$\int_a^b \{\alpha_1(x) - y_1(x)\} z_{i-1}(x)\, dx = 0 \qquad (i = 1, 2, \ldots, k).$$

we can show by elementary transformations that

$$c_{1i} = a_{i-1} \qquad (i = 1, 2, \ldots, k).$$

If we keep this in mind, we see that the first approximation obtained by means of the Sokolov method will be of the form

$$y_1(x) = z_0(x) + \lambda a_0 z_1(x) + \cdots + \lambda a_{k-1} z_k(x). \quad (2.133)$$

We note that we must carry out exactly the same number of calculations to obtain the approximate solutions $y_1(x)$ and $y_k{}^*(x)$.

Example 11. Find the solution of the integral equation

$$y(x) = \frac{x}{2} + \frac{\pi^2}{4} \int_0^1 K(x, \xi) y(\xi)\, d\xi,$$

where

$$K(x, \xi) = \begin{cases} \frac{1}{2}(2 - \xi)x, & x \leqslant \xi, \\ \frac{1}{2}(2 - x)\xi, & x \geqslant \xi. \end{cases}$$

The exact solution of this equation is

$$y(x) = \sin \frac{\pi}{2} x.$$

For $k = 2$, we have on the basis of formulas (2.130) and (2.132)

$$z_0(x) = \frac{x}{2}, \qquad z_1(x) = \tfrac{1}{12}(2x - x^3),$$

$$z_2(x) = \tfrac{1}{720}(3x^5 - 20x^3 + 31x),$$

$$(z_0, z_0) = \tfrac{1}{12}, \qquad (z_0, z_1) = \tfrac{1}{12} \cdot \tfrac{7}{30}, \qquad (z_0, z_2) = \tfrac{1}{12} \cdot \tfrac{71}{1260},$$

$$(z_1, z_1) = \tfrac{1}{12} \cdot \tfrac{71}{1260}, \qquad (z_1, z_2) = \tfrac{1}{12} \cdot \tfrac{517}{37800},$$

$$\begin{aligned} \alpha_0{}^* + \tfrac{7}{30}\alpha_1{}^* + \tfrac{71}{1260} &= 0, \\ 7\alpha_0{}^* + \tfrac{71}{42}\alpha_1{}^* + \tfrac{517}{1260} &= 0. \end{aligned} \quad (2.134)$$

When we solve the system (2.134) we obtain

$$\alpha_0 = \tfrac{8}{945}, \qquad \alpha_1 = -\tfrac{5}{18}.$$

Consequently, from formulas (2.131) and (2.129), we have

$$\alpha_0 = \frac{15120 - 1050\pi^2}{15120 - 1050\pi^2 + 8\pi^4}, \qquad \alpha_1 = \frac{3780\pi^2}{15120 - 1050\pi^2 + 8\pi^4},$$

$$y_2{}^*(x) = \frac{105}{15120 - 1050\pi^2 + 8\pi^4}(72x - \pi^2 x - 3\pi^2 x^3)$$

$$\approx 1.5527x - 0.5616x^3.$$

The first approximation obtained by means of the Sokolov method is, according to (2.133), of the form

$$y_1(x) = \frac{x}{2} + \frac{\pi^2}{8} \cdot \frac{2520 - 175\pi^2}{15120 - 1050\pi^2 + 8\pi^4}(2x - x^3)$$

$$+ \frac{\pi^2}{16} \cdot \frac{21\pi^2}{15120 - 1050\pi^2 + 8\pi^4}(3x^5 - 20x^3 + 31x)$$

$$\approx 1.5692x - 0.6385x^3 + 0.0693x^5.$$

TABLE VIII

x	$y(x)$	$y_1(x)$	$y_2{}^*(x)$	$y(x) - y_1(x)$	$y(x) - y_2{}^*(x)$
0.00	0.0000	0.0000	0.0000	0.0000	0.0000
0.25	0.3827	0.3824	0.3794	0.0003	0.0033
0.50	0.7071	0.7070	0.7062	0.0001	0.0009
0.75	0.9239	0.9243	0.9277	−0.0004	−0.0038
1.00	1.0000	1.0000	0.9911	0.0000	0.0089

It is clear from Table VIII that the first approximation by the Sokolov method is considerably better than the approximation obtained by the method of moments. As was noted above, the number of calculations is the same for both methods.

CHAPTER **III**

Application of the Method to Systems of Linear Integral and Differential Equations

1. Systems of Linear Integral Equations in the Space $L^p(a, b)$

1. In this section, we shall apply Sokolov's method to systems of linear integral equations of the form

$$y_m(x) = f_m(x) + \lambda \sum_{l=1}^{N} \int_a^b K_{ml}(x, \xi) y_l(\xi)\, d\xi \tag{3.1}$$

$$(m = 1, 2, \ldots, N),$$

about which it is assumed that:

(1) the complex parameter λ is a regular value,

(2) the interval (a, b) is either finite or infinite,

(3) N is either finite or infinite, and

(4) the complex-valued functions $f_m(x)$ and the kernels $K_{ml}(x, \xi)$ with real arguments x and ξ satisfy the following conditions:

$$\left\{\int_a^b \left[\sum_{l=1}^{N} \left(\int_a^b |K_{ml}(x, \xi)|^q\, d\xi\right)^{1/q}\right]^p dx\right\}^{1/p} < \infty, \tag{3.2}$$

$$\left\{\int_a^b |f_m(x)|^p\, dx\right\}^{1/p} < \infty, \qquad \frac{1}{p} + \frac{1}{q} = 1 \qquad (m = 1, 2, \ldots, N).$$

The principle of the Sokolov method consists in this case in determining the nth approximation from the following systems of equations:

$$y_{mn}(x) = f_m(x) + \lambda \sum_{l=1}^{N} \int_a^b K_{ml}(x, \xi) y_{ln-1}(\xi)\, d\xi + \lambda \sum_{l=1}^{N^*} \int_a^b K_{ml}(x, \xi) \alpha_{ln}(\xi)\, d\xi \quad (m = 1, 2, \ldots, N), \tag{3.3}$$

where

$$\alpha_{mn}(x) = \int_a^b S_{mk_m}(x, \xi) \delta_{mn}(\xi)\, d\xi, \tag{3.4}$$

$$\delta_{mn}(x) = y_{mn}(x) - y_{mn-1}(x) \qquad (m = 1, 2, \ldots, N^*). \tag{3.5}$$

Here, $N^* \leqslant N$ and $S_{mk_m}(x, \xi)$ are arbitrary functions satisfying the conditions

$$S_{mk_m}(x, \xi) = \int_a^b S_{mk_m}(x, t) S_{mk_m}(t, \xi)\, dt, \tag{3.6}$$

$$\left\{ \int_a^b \left[\int_a^b |S_{mk_m}(x, \xi)|^q\, d\xi \right]^{p/q} dx \right\}^{1/p} < \infty, \tag{3.7}$$

$$v(x) = \lim_{k_m \to \infty} \int_a^b S_{mk_m}(x, \xi) v(\xi)\, d\xi, \qquad v(x) \in L^p. \tag{3.8}$$

As our zeroth approximation $y_{10}(x), \ldots, y_{N0}(x)$, we may take an arbitrary system of functions in the space L^p.

On the basis of Eqs. (3.4) and (3.6), the nth approximation (3.3) can be written in the form

$$y_{mn}(x) = f_m(x) + \lambda \sum_{l=1}^{N} \int_a^b K_{ml}(x, \xi) y_{ln-1}(\xi)\, d\xi + \lambda \sum_{l=1}^{N^*} \int_a^b M_{ml}(x, \xi) \alpha_{ln}(\xi)\, d\xi \quad (m = 1, 2, \ldots, N), \tag{3.9}$$

where

$$M_{ml}(x, \xi) = \int_a^b K_{ml}(x, t) S_{lk_l}(t, \xi)\, dt \quad (m = 1, 2, \ldots, N^*). \tag{3.10}$$

If we substitute (3.9) in (3.5), and then substitute the result in (3.4), we obtain a system of linear integral equations for determining the functions $\alpha_{mn}(x)$:

$$\alpha_{mn}(x) = g_{mn-1}(x) + \lambda \sum_{l=1}^{N^*} \int_a^b H_{ml}(x, \xi)\alpha_{ln}(\xi)\, d\xi, \tag{3.11}$$

where

$$H_{ml}(x, \xi) = \int_a^b S_{mk_m}(x, t)M_{ml}(t, \xi)\, dt, \tag{3.12}$$

$$g_{mn-1}(x) = \int_a^b S_{mk_m}(x, \xi)\varepsilon_{mn-1}(\xi)\, d\xi, \tag{3.13}$$

$$\begin{aligned}\varepsilon_{mn-1}(x) &= f_m(x) - y_{mn-1}(x)\\ &\qquad + \lambda \sum_{l=1}^{N} \int_a^b K_{ml}(x, \xi)y_{ln-1}(\xi)\, d\xi.\end{aligned} \tag{3.14}$$

From the system (3.11) (which we assume to have a solution), we find that

$$\alpha_{mn}(x) = \sum_{i=1}^{N^*} \int_a^b R_{im}(x, \xi, \lambda)g_{in-1}(\xi)\, d\xi. \tag{3.15}$$

The functions $R_{lm}(x, \xi, \lambda)$ satisfy the system of integral equations

$$\begin{aligned}R_{lm}(x, \xi, \lambda) &= \delta_{ml}S_{lk_l}(x, \xi)\\ &\qquad + \lambda \sum_{i=1}^{N^*} \int_a^b H_{mi}(x, t)R_{li}(t, \xi, \lambda)\, dt,\end{aligned} \tag{3.16}$$

$$\delta_{ml} = \begin{cases}1, & m = l,\\ 0, & m \neq l\end{cases} \qquad (m, l = 1, 2, \ldots, N^*),$$

also,

$$\begin{aligned}R_{lm}(x, \xi, \lambda) &= \int_a^b S_{mk_m}(x, t)R_{lm}(t, \xi, \lambda)\, dt\\ &= \int_a^b R_{lm}(x, t, \lambda)S_{lk_l}(t, \xi)\, dt.\end{aligned} \tag{3.17}$$

When we substitute the value of $\alpha_n(x)$ given by formula (3.15) in (3.9), we finally obtain the expression for the nth approximation.

2. Let us find a sufficient condition for the convergence of the sequences (3.9) to the solution of the system of Eqs. (3.1).

On the basis of formulas (3.3) and (3.5), we have

$$\begin{aligned}\delta_{mn}(x) &= \lambda\sum_{l=1}^{N^*}\int_a^b K_{ml}(x,\xi)\{\delta_{ln-1}(\xi)-\alpha_{ln-1}(\xi)\}\,d\xi \\ &\quad + \lambda\sum_{l=N^*+1}^{N}\int_a^b K_{ml}(x,\xi)\delta_{ln-1}(\xi)\,d\xi \\ &\quad + \lambda\sum_{l=1}^{N^*}\int_a^b K_{ml}(x,\xi)\alpha_{ln}(\xi)\,d\xi \\ &= \lambda\sum_{l=1}^{N^*}\int_a^b \{K_{ml}(x,\xi)-M_{ml}(x,\xi)\} \\ &\quad \times \{\delta_{ln-1}(\xi)-\alpha_{ln-1}(\xi)\}\,d\xi \\ &\quad + \lambda\sum_{l=N^*+1}^{N}\int_a^b K_{ml}(x,\xi)\delta_{ln-1}(\xi)\,d\xi \\ &\quad + \lambda\sum_{l=1}^{N^*}\int_a^b K_{ml}(x,\xi)\alpha_{ln}(\xi)\,d\xi, \end{aligned} \tag{3.18}$$

since, by virtue of (3.4), (3.6), and (3.10),

$$\begin{aligned}&\int_a^b M_{ml}(x,\xi)\{\delta_{ln-1}(\xi)-\alpha_{ln-1}(\xi)\}\,d\xi \\ &\quad = \int_b^a\int_b^a K_{ml}(x,t)S_{lk_l}(t,\xi)\{\delta_{ln-1}(\xi)-\alpha_{ln-1}(\xi)\}\,dt\,d\xi \qquad (3.19) \\ &\quad = \int_a^b K_{ml}(x,t)\int_a^b S_{lk_l}(t,\xi)\{\delta_{ln-1}(\xi)-\alpha_{ln-1}(\xi)\}\,d\xi\,dt = 0.\end{aligned}$$

We introduce the notations

$$F_{ml}(x,\xi) = \begin{cases} K_{ml}(x,\xi)-M_{ml}(x,\xi), & l \leqslant N^*, \\ K_{ml}(x,\xi), & l > N^*\ (m=1,2,\ldots,N), \end{cases} \tag{3.20}$$

$$z_{mn}(x) = \begin{cases} \delta_{mn}(x)-\alpha_{mn}(x), & m \leqslant N^*, \\ \delta_{mn}(x), & m > N^*. \end{cases} \tag{3.21}$$

Then,

$$\delta_{mn}(x) = \lambda \sum_{l=1}^{N} \int_a^b F_{ml}(x, \xi) z_{ln-1}(\xi)\, d\xi + \lambda \sum_{l=1}^{N^*} \int_a^b K_{ml}(x, \xi) \alpha_{ln}(\xi)\, d\xi. \tag{3.22}$$

By using formulas (3.3) and (3.19) and the notations (3.20) and (3.21), we may represent the functions $\varepsilon_{mn-1}(x)$ defined by Eq. (3.14) in the form

$$\varepsilon_{mn-1}(x) = \lambda \sum_{l=1}^{N} \int_a^b F_{ml}(x, \xi) z_{ln-1}(\xi)\, d\xi. \tag{3.23}$$

On the basis of formulas (3.13), (3.15), (3.17), and (3.23), we have

$$\alpha_{mn}(x) = \lambda \sum_{l=1}^{N} \sum_{i=1}^{N^*} \int_a^b \int_a^b R_{im}(x, t, \lambda) F_{il}(t, \xi) z_{ln-1}(\xi)\, dt\, d\xi. \tag{3.24}$$

If we now substitute (3.24) in (3.22), we finally obtain

$$\delta_{mn}(x) = \sum_{l=1}^{N} \int_a^b \Omega_{ml}(x, \xi, \lambda) z_{ln-1}(\xi)\, d\xi, \tag{3.25}$$

where

$$\Omega_{ml}(x, \xi, \lambda) = \lambda F_{ml}(x, \xi) + \lambda^2 \sum_{i=1}^{N^*} \sum_{j=1}^{N^*} \int_a^b \int_a^b K_{mj}(x, \eta) R_{ij}(\eta, t, \lambda) F_{il}(t, \xi)\, d\alpha\, dt. \tag{3.26}$$

The functions $\Omega_{ml}(x, \xi, \lambda)$ satisfy the system of equations [cf. (1.29)]

$$\Omega_{ml}(x, \xi, \lambda) = \lambda F_{ml}(x, \xi) + \lambda \sum_{s=1}^{N^*} \int_a^b M_{ms}(x, t) \Omega_{sl}(t, \xi, \lambda)\, dt. \tag{3.27}$$

If we substitute (3.25) in (3.4) and then substitute the results in (3.21), we obtain

$$z_{mn}(x) = \sum_{l=1}^{N} \int_a^b L_{ml}(x, \xi, \lambda) z_{ln-1}(\xi)\, d\xi, \tag{3.28}$$

where

$$L_{ml}(x, \xi, \lambda) = \begin{cases} \Omega_{ml}(x, \xi, \lambda) - W_{ml}(x, \xi, \lambda), & m \leqslant N^*, \\ \Omega_{ml}(x, \xi, \lambda), & m > N^* \ (l = 1, 2, \ldots, N), \end{cases} \tag{3.29}$$

$$W_{ml}(x, \xi, \lambda) = \int_a^b S_{mk_m}(x, t)\Omega_{ml}(t, \xi, \lambda)\, dt.$$

THEOREM 12. *If conditions* (3.2) *are satisfied and* $\Lambda(\lambda) < 1$, *where*

$$\Lambda(\lambda) = \sup_m \left\{ \int_a^b \left[\sum_{l=1}^N \left(\int_a^b |L_{ml}(x, \xi, \lambda)|^q \, d\xi \right)^{1/q} \right]^p dx \right\}^{1/p}, \tag{3.30}$$

then there exists a unique solution y_m^* (*for* $m = 1, 2, \ldots, N$) *of the system of integral equations* (3.1) *and the sequences* (3.9) *converge coordinatewise to this solution in the* L^p *norm.*

Proof. From the relations (3.25) and (3.28), we have

$$\left\{ \int_a^b |\delta_{mn}(x)|^p \, dx \right\}^{1/p} \leqslant \Omega_m(\lambda) \sup_l \left\{ \int_a^b |z_{ln-1}(\xi)|^p \, d\xi \right\}^{1/p}, \tag{3.31}$$

where

$$\Omega_m(\lambda) = \left\{ \int_a^b \left[\sum_{l=1}^N \left(\int_a^b |\Omega_{ml}(x, \xi, \lambda)|^q \, d\xi \right)^{1/q} \right]^p dx \right\}^{1/p}, \tag{3.32}$$

$$\begin{aligned} \sup_m \left\{ \int_a^b |z_{mn}(x)|^p \, dx \right\}^{1/p} &\leqslant \Lambda(\lambda) \sup_l \left\{ \int_a^b |z_{ln-1}(x)|^p \, dx \right\}^{1/p} \\ &\leqslant \Lambda^{n-1}(\lambda) \sup_l \left\{ \int_a^b |z_{l1}(x)|^p \, dx \right\}^{1/p}. \end{aligned} \tag{3.33}$$

When we substitute (3.33) in (3.31), we obtain

$$\left\{ \int_a^b |\delta_{mn}(x)|^p \, dx \right\}^{1/p} \leqslant \Omega_m(\lambda)\Lambda^{n-2}(\lambda) \sup_l \left\{ \int_a^b |z_{l1}(x)|^p \, dx \right\}^{1/p}.$$

Consequently, if $\Lambda(\lambda) < 1$, then

$$\left\{ \int_a^b |\delta_{mn}(x)|^p \, dx \right\}^{1/p} \to 0 \quad \text{as} \quad n \to \infty$$

(for $m = 1, 2, \ldots, N$).

Therefore, since the space L^p is complete, the limit $y_m^*(x)$ (for $m = 1, 2, \dots, N$) of the sequences (3.9) exists. The functions $y_m^*(x)$ constitute a solution of the system (3.1). This follows from relations (3.3) and (3.4). The uniqueness of this solution follows from Theorem 1.

THEOREM 13. *If conditions* (1)–(4) *are satisfied, then* $k_m \to \infty$ *and* $\Lambda(\lambda) \to 0$ *as* $N^* \to N$.

The proof of this theorem is analogous to the proof of Theorem 3.

It follows from Theorem 13 that when conditions (1)–(4) are satisfied, a number N^* and functions $S_{mk_m}(x, \xi)$ can be chosen so that the inequality $\Lambda(\lambda) < 1$ will always be satisfied.

If $S_{mk_m}(x, \xi) \equiv 0$, the Sokolov method reduces to the ordinary method of successive approximations. In this case, we obtain from the sufficient condition for convergence of the Sokolov method a sufficient condition for convergence of the method of successive approximations:

$$\Lambda(\lambda) = \sup_m \left\{ \int_a^b \left[\sum_{l=1}^N \left(\int_a^b |\lambda K_{ml}(x, \xi)|^q \, d\xi \right)^{1/q} \right]^p dx \right\}^{1/p} < 1. \quad (3.34)$$

By using the results of Theorems 6 and 7, we can show that if (3.34) is satisfied for $p = q = 2$, then, for an arbitrary choice of Hermitian symmetric functions $S_{mk_m}(x, \xi)$ and of a number $N^* \leqslant N$, the sequences (3.9) always converge to the solution of the system (3.1).

3. Suppose that

$$\Delta_{mn}(x) = y_m^*(x) - y_{mn}(x),$$

where $y_m^*(x)$ and $y_{mn}(x)$ are, respectively, the exact and approximate solutions of the system (3.1). Then, in a manner analogous to that of Section 4 of Chapter I, we can obtain the following estimates of the error:

$$|\Delta_{mn}(x)| \leqslant \frac{\Omega_m(x, \lambda)}{1 - \Lambda(\lambda)} \sup_l \left\{ \int_a^b |z_{ln}(\xi)|^p \, d\xi \right\}^{1/p}, \quad (3.35)$$

$$\Omega_m(x, \lambda) = \sum_{l=1}^{N} \left\{ \int_a^b |\Omega_{ml}(x, \xi, \lambda)|^q \, d\xi \right\}^{1/q}, \tag{3.36}$$

$$|\Delta_{mn}(x)| \leqslant \frac{\Omega_m(x, \lambda)\Lambda^{n-1}(\lambda)}{1 - \Lambda(\lambda)} \sup_l \left\{ \int_a^b |z_{l1}(\xi)|^p \, d\xi \right\}^{1/p}, \tag{3.37}$$

$$I_{mn}(x) = \frac{|\Delta_{mn}(x)|}{|y_m{}^*(x)|} \leqslant \frac{100|\Delta_{mn}(x)|\,\%}{|y_{mn}(x)| - |\Delta_{mn}(x)|} \quad (n \geqslant n_0), \tag{3.38}$$

$$I_{mn}(x) \leqslant \theta\Omega_m(x, \lambda)\Lambda^{n-1}(\lambda)$$
$$[y_{10}(x) = \cdots = y_{N0}(x) = 0; \qquad 0 \leqslant \theta \leqslant 1]. \tag{3.39}$$

4. Suppose that $\{\varphi_{ms}(x)\}$ and $\{\Psi_{ms}(x)\}$ (for $s = 1, 2, \ldots, N^*$) are systems of linearly independent functions belonging, respectively, to the spaces L^p and L^q. We determine the successive approximations in accordance with the formulas

$$y_{mn}(x) = f_m(x) + \lambda \sum_{l=1}^{N} \int_a^b K_{ml}(x, \xi) y_{ln-1}(\xi) \, d\xi$$
$$+ \lambda \sum_{l=1}^{N^*} \int_a^b K_{ml}(x, \xi) \alpha_{ln}(\xi) \, d\xi \qquad (m = 1, 2, \ldots, N), \tag{3.40}$$

$$\alpha_{mn}(x) = \sum_{s=1}^{k_m} c_{mn}^{(s)} \varphi_{ms}(x) \qquad (m = 1, 2, \ldots, N^*), \tag{3.41}$$

and the coefficients $c_{mn}^{(s)}$ from the conditions

$$\int_a^b \{\alpha_{mn}(x) - \delta_{mn}(x)\} \overline{\psi_{ms}(x)} \, dx = 0$$
$$(s = 1, 2, \ldots, k_m; \qquad m = 1, 2, \ldots, N^*). \tag{3.42}$$

In a manner analogous to what was done in paragraph 4 of Section 1 of Chapter II, one can show that the algorithm proposed here is a special case of the algorithm defined by formulas (3.3)–(3.5). Here,

$$S_{mk_m}(x, \xi) = \sum_{i=1}^{k_m} \sum_{j=1}^{k_m} \frac{D_{ij}^{(m)}}{D_k^{(m)}} \varphi_{mj}(x)\overline{\psi_{mi}(\xi)}, \tag{3.43}$$

$$D_k^{(m)} = \begin{vmatrix} \gamma_{11}^{(m)} & \cdots & \gamma_{1k_m}^{(m)} \\ & \cdots & \\ \gamma_{k_m1}^{(m)} & \cdots & \gamma_{k_mk_m}^{(m)} \end{vmatrix},$$

$$\gamma_{ij}^{(m)} = \int_a^b \varphi_{mj}(x)\overline{\psi_{mi}(x)}\, dx,$$

and the $D_{ij}^{(m)}$ are the cofactors of the elements $\gamma_{ij}^{(m)}$.

When the systems of functions $\{\varphi_{ms}(x)\}$ and $\{\psi_{ms}(x)\}$ are biorthogonal, that is, when

$$\int_a^b \varphi_{mj}(x)\overline{\psi_{mi}(x)}\, dx = \begin{cases} \gamma_i^{(m)} \neq 0, & i = j, \\ 0, & i \neq j \qquad (m = 1, 2, \ldots, N^*), \end{cases}$$

the formulas (3.42) and (3.43) simplify and take the form

$$c_{mn}^{(s)} = \frac{1}{\gamma_s^{(m)}} \int_a^b \overline{\psi_{ms}(x)}\, \delta_{mn}(x)\, dx, \tag{3.44}$$

$$S_{mk_m}(x, \xi) = \sum_{s=1}^{k_m} \frac{1}{\gamma_s^{(m)}} \varphi_{ms}(x)\, \overline{\psi_{ms}(\xi)}. \tag{3.45}$$

In the case of the space L^2, the coefficients $c_{mn}^{(s)}$ can also be determined from the condition for the minimum of the functionals

$$\int_a^b \{\alpha_{mn}(x) - \delta_{mn}(x)\}^2\, dx \qquad (m = 1, 2, \ldots, N^*).$$

Example 12. Let us consider the system of two linear integral equations

$$y_1(x) = 1 + \lambda \int_0^1 x\xi y_1(\xi)\, d\xi + \lambda \int_0^1 x\xi^2 y_2(\xi)\, d\xi,$$

$$y_2(x) = x + \lambda \int_0^1 x^2\xi y_1(\xi)\, d\xi + \lambda \int_0^1 x^2\xi^2 y_2(\xi)\, d\xi,$$

for which $\lambda = 15/8$ is an eigenvalue.

Suppose that $N^* = 2$ and that

$$S_{11}(x, \xi) = S_{21}(x, \xi) = 1.$$

Then, on the basis of formulas (3.10) and (3.20), we have

$$M_{11}(x, \xi) = \frac{x}{2}, \qquad M_{12}(x, \xi) = \frac{x}{3}, \qquad M_{21}(x, \xi) = \frac{x^2}{2},$$

$$M_{22}(x, \xi) = \frac{x^2}{3}, \qquad F_{11}(x, \xi) = x(\xi - \tfrac{1}{2}),$$

$$F_{12}(x, \xi) = x(\xi^2 - \tfrac{1}{3}), \qquad F_{21}(x, \xi) = x^2(\xi - \tfrac{1}{2}),$$

$$F_{22}(x, \xi) = x^2(\xi^2 - \tfrac{1}{3}).$$

Consequently, for determining the functions $\Omega_{ml}(x, \xi, \lambda)$, we have, according to (3.27), the system of equations

$$\Omega_{11}(x, \xi, \lambda) = \lambda x(\xi - \tfrac{1}{2}) + \lambda \int_0^1 \frac{x}{2} \Omega_{11}(t, \xi, \lambda)\, dt$$

$$+ \lambda \int_0^1 \frac{x}{3} \Omega_{21}(t, \xi, \lambda)\, dt,$$

$$\Omega_{21}(x, \xi, \lambda) = \lambda x^2(\xi - \tfrac{1}{2}) + \lambda \int_0^1 \frac{x^2}{2} \Omega_{11}(t, \xi, \lambda)\, dt$$

$$+ \lambda \int_0^1 \frac{x^2}{3} \Omega_{21}(t, \xi, \lambda)\, dt,$$

$$\Omega_{12}(x, \xi, \lambda) = \lambda x(\xi^2 - \tfrac{1}{3}) + \lambda \int_0^1 \frac{x}{2} \Omega_{12}(t, \xi, \lambda)\, dt$$

$$+ \lambda \int_0^1 \frac{x}{3} \Omega_{22}(t, \xi, \lambda)\, dt,$$

$$\Omega_{22}(x, \xi, \lambda) = \lambda x^2(\xi^2 - \tfrac{1}{3}) + \lambda \int_0^1 \frac{x^2}{2} \Omega_{12}(t, \xi, \lambda)\, dt$$

$$+ \lambda \int_0^1 \frac{x^2}{3} \Omega_{22}(t, \xi, \lambda)\, dt,$$

from which we get

$$\Omega_{11}(x, \xi, \lambda) = \frac{36\lambda}{36 - 13\lambda} x(\xi - \tfrac{1}{2}),$$

$$\Omega_{12}(x, \xi, \lambda) = \frac{36\lambda}{36 - 13\lambda} x(\xi^2 - \tfrac{1}{3}),$$

$$\Omega_{21}(x, \xi, \lambda) = \frac{36\lambda}{36 - 13\lambda} x^2(\xi - \tfrac{1}{2}),$$

$$\Omega_{22}(x, \xi, \lambda) = \frac{36\lambda}{36 - 13\lambda} x^2(\xi^2 - \tfrac{1}{3}).$$

On the basis of formula (3.29), we obtain

$$L_{11}(x, \xi, \lambda) = \frac{36\lambda}{36 - 13\lambda} (x - \tfrac{1}{2})(\xi - \tfrac{1}{2}),$$

$$L_{12}(x, \xi, \lambda) = \frac{36\lambda}{36 - 13\lambda} (x - \tfrac{1}{2})(\xi^2 - \tfrac{1}{3}),$$

$$L_{21}(x, \xi, \lambda) = \frac{36\lambda}{36 - 13\lambda} (x^2 - \tfrac{1}{3})(\xi - \tfrac{1}{2}),$$

$$L_{22}(x, \xi, \lambda) = \frac{36\lambda}{36 - 13\lambda} (x^2 - \tfrac{1}{3})(\xi^2 - \tfrac{1}{3}).$$

For the present example, a necessary and sufficient condition for convergence of the method (Theorem 1) is the condition that

$$\frac{31|\lambda|}{5|36 - 13\lambda|} < 1,$$

from which it follows that the method converges for all values of the parameter λ belonging to the intervals $(-\infty, 15/8)$ and $(90/17, \infty)$. The method of successive approximations converges only in the interval $(-15/8, 15/8)$.

Suppose that $\lambda = -2$. Then, the system of equations

$$\begin{aligned} y_1(x) &= 1 - 2\int_0^1 x\xi y_1(\xi)\, d\xi - 2\int_0^1 x\xi^2 y_2(\xi)\, d\xi, \\ y_2(x) &= x - 2\int_0^1 x^2\xi y_1(\xi)\, d\xi - 2\int_0^1 x^2\xi^2 y_2(\xi)\, d\xi \end{aligned} \tag{3.46}$$

has the solution

$$y_1(x) = 1 - \tfrac{45}{62}x, \qquad y_2(x) = x - \tfrac{45}{62}x^2.$$

Let us apply this method to the system (3.46). In other words, let us take as our first approximation [see formulas (3.40), (3.41), and (3.44)]

$$y_{11}(x) = 1 - c_{11}x - \tfrac{2}{3}c_{21}x,$$
$$y_{21}(x) = x - c_{11}x^2 - \tfrac{2}{3}c_{21}x^2,$$
$$[\alpha_{11}(x) = c_{11}, \qquad \alpha_{21}(x) = c_{21}],$$
$$c_{11} = \int_0^1 y_{11}(x)\,dx, \qquad c_{21} = \int_0^1 y_{21}(x)\,dx.$$

For determining c_{11} and c_{21}, we obtain the system

$$c_{11} = 1 - \frac{c_{11}}{2} - \frac{c_{21}}{3},$$

$$c_{21} = \frac{1}{2} - \frac{c_{11}}{3} - \frac{2c_{21}}{9},$$

from which we get $c_{11} = 19/31$ and $c_{21} = 15/62$.

Thus, the first approximation is given by the formulas

$$y_{11}(x) = 1 - \tfrac{24}{31}x, \qquad y_{21}(x) = x - \tfrac{24}{31}x^2.$$

For our second approximation, we have

$$y_{12}(x) = 1 - \tfrac{209}{310}x - c_{12}x - \tfrac{2}{3}c_{22}x,$$
$$y_{22}(x) = x - \tfrac{209}{310}x - c_{12}x^2 - \tfrac{2}{3}c_{22}x^2,$$
$$c_{12} = \int_0^1 \delta_{12}(x)\,dx, \qquad c_{22} = \int_0^1 \delta_{22}(x)\,dx,$$

$$\delta_{12}(x) = \frac{x}{10} - c_{12}x - \tfrac{2}{3}c_{22}x,$$

$$\delta_{22}(x) = \frac{x^2}{10} - c_{12}x^2 - \tfrac{2}{3}c_{22}x^2,$$

$$c_{12} = \frac{1}{20} - \frac{c_{12}}{2} - \frac{c_{22}}{3},$$

$$c_{22} = \frac{1}{30} - \frac{c_{12}}{3} - \frac{2c_{22}}{9},$$

$$c_{12} = \tfrac{9}{310}, \qquad c_{22} = \tfrac{6}{310},$$
$$y_{12}(x) = 1 - \tfrac{222}{310}x, \qquad y_{22}(x) = x - \tfrac{222}{310}x^2.$$

If we continue this process further, we get as our nth approximation

$$y_{1n}(x) = 1 - \frac{45}{62}x + \frac{3}{62}\cdot\frac{(-1)^n}{5^{n-1}}x,$$

$$y_{2n}(x) = x - \frac{45}{62}x^2 + \frac{3}{62}\cdot\frac{(-1)^n}{5^{n-1}}x^2.$$

On the basis of formulas (3.30) and (3.36),

$$\Lambda_1(-2) = 0.1967, \qquad \Lambda_2(-2) = 0.2032.$$

Consequently, $\Lambda(-2) = 0.2032$ and

$$\Omega_1(x, -2) = 0.6814x, \qquad \Omega_2(x, -2) = 0.6814x^2.$$

According to formula (3.35),

$$|\Delta_{1n}(x)| \leqslant 1.534\cdot\frac{3x}{62\cdot 5^{n-1}}, \qquad |\Delta_{2n}(x)| \leqslant 1.534\cdot\frac{3x^2}{62\cdot 5^{n-1}}$$

$$(n = 2, 3, 4, \ldots).$$

The exact values are

$$|\Delta_{1n}(x)| = \frac{3x}{62\cdot 5^{n-1}}, \qquad |\Delta_{2n}(x)| = \frac{3x^2}{62\cdot 5^{n-1}}.$$

2. Systems of Linear Differential Equations

1. Consider the boundary-value problem

$$A_m y_m(x) = f_m(x) + \lambda \sum_{l=1}^{\infty} B_{ml} y_l(x), \tag{3.47}$$

$$U_{m_r}(y_m) = 0 \qquad (r = 1, 2, \ldots, N_m; \quad m = 1, 2, 3, \ldots), \tag{3.48}$$

where

$$A_m = \sum_{\nu=0}^{N_m} a_m^{(\nu)}(x)\,\frac{d^\nu}{dx^\nu},$$

$$B_{ml} = \sum_{\nu=0}^{N_l^*} b_{ml}^{(\nu)}(x)\,\frac{d^\nu}{dx^\nu},$$

$$U_{m_r}(y_m) = \sum_{\nu=0}^{N_m-1} [\bar{a}_{m_r}^{(\nu)} y_m^{(\nu)}(a) + \bar{b}_{m_r}^{(\nu)} y_m^{(\nu)}(b)],$$

and for every fixed $m = l$, $N_m > N_l^*$ $(l = 1, 2, 3, \ldots)$.

We make the following assumptions concerning the system (3.47) and the boundary conditions (3.48):

(1) For a given value of the parameter λ, the problem (3.47)–(3.48) has a solution.

(2) The complex-valued coefficients $a_m^{(\nu)}(x)$, and $b_{ml}^{(\nu)}(x)$ and the functions $f_m(x)$ of the real variable x are continuous on the finite interval $[a, b]$.

(3) For an arbitrary system of functions $z_l(x)$ (for $l = 1, 2, 3, \ldots$) belonging to the classes $C^{(N_l*)}$, respectively, the series

$$\sum_{l=1}^{\infty} B_{ml} z_l(x) \qquad (m = 1, 2, 3, \ldots)$$

converge uniformly.

(4) The problem

$$A_m w_m(x) = 0, \tag{3.49}$$

$$U_{m_r}(w_m) = 0 \qquad (r = 1, 2, \ldots, N_m) \tag{3.50}$$

has only the trivial solution.

(5) The Green's function $G_m(x, \xi)$ of the problem (3.49)–(3.50) can be found in explicit form.

Let us apply the method described in this monograph to the problem (3.47)–(3.48). In other words, let us determine the nth approximation from the following system of equations:

$$\begin{aligned} A_m y_{mn}(x) = f_m(x) &+ \lambda \sum_{l=1}^{\infty} B_{ml} y_{ln-1}(x) \\ &+ \lambda \sum_{l=1}^{N^*} B_{ml} \alpha_{ln}(x), \end{aligned} \tag{3.51}$$

$$U_{m_r}(y_{mn}) = 0 \qquad (m = 1, 2, 3, \ldots; \quad r = 1, 2, \ldots, N_m) \tag{3.52}$$

where

$$\alpha_{sn}(x) = \sum_{i=1}^{k_s} c_{ni}^{(s)} \varphi_{si}(x) \qquad (s = 1, 2, \ldots, N^*). \tag{3.53}$$

We determine the functions $\varphi_{is}(x)$ from the following problems:

$$A_s \varphi_{si}(x) = \psi_{si}(x) \qquad (s = 1, 2, \ldots, N^*; \quad i = 1, 2, \ldots, k_s), \tag{3.54}$$

$$U_{s_r}(\varphi_{si}) = 0 \qquad (r = 1, 2, \ldots, N_s), \tag{3.55}$$

where the $\{\psi_{si}(x)\}$ are arbitrary systems of linearly independent continuous functions on the interval $[a, b]$.

We determine the zeroth approximation from the problem

$$A_m y_{0m}(x) = g_m(x) \qquad (m = 1, 2, 3, \ldots), \tag{3.56}$$

where

$$U_{m_r}(y_{m0}) = 0 \qquad (r = 1, 2, \ldots, N_m), \tag{3.57}$$

and the $g_m(x)$ are arbitrary continuous functions on the interval $[a, b.]$ [In practice, we may take $g_m(x) = 0$ or $g_m(x) = f_m(x)$.]

The coefficients $c_{ni}^{(s)}$ are determined from the conditions

$$\int_a^b \overline{\varphi_{sj}(x)} A_s[\delta_{sn}(x) - \alpha_{sn}(x)]\, dx = 0 \qquad (j = 1, 2, \ldots, k_s), \tag{3.58}$$

where

$$\delta_{sn}(x) = y_{sn}(x) - y_{sn-1}(x) \qquad (s = 1, 2, \ldots, N^*). \tag{3.59}$$

They can also be determined by using the method of least squares, the Ritz method, the method of collocations, the method of subregions, and other methods.

On the basis of formulas (3.51) and (3.59), we have

$$A_s\delta_{sn}(x) = \lambda \sum_{l=1}^{\infty} B_{sl}\delta_{ln-1}(x) + \lambda \sum_{l=1}^{N^*} B_{sl}[\alpha_{ln}(x) - \alpha_{l_{n-1}}(x)]. \tag{3.60}$$

If we substitute (3.60) in (3.58) and make use of (3.53) and (3.54), we obtain a system of linear algebraic equations with $k_1 + k_2 + \cdots + k_{N^*}$ unknowns, from which we determine the unknown coefficients $c_{ni}^{(s)}$. When we substitute the values of $c_{ni}^{(s)}$ in (3.53) and then substitute the result in (3.51) and finally solve (3.51)–(3.52), we obtain the nth approximation $y_{mn}(x)$ (for $m = 1, 2, 3, \ldots$).

2. Let us define

$$A_m y_m(x) = v_m(x). \tag{3.61}$$

$$U_{m_r}(y_m) = 0 \qquad (m = 1, 2, 3, \ldots; \quad r = 1, 2, \ldots, N_m). \tag{3.62}$$

Then, the problem (3.47)–(3.48) reduces to a system of integral equations of the form

$$v_m(x) = f_m(x) + \lambda \sum_{l=1}^{\infty} \int_a^b K_{ml}(x, \xi) v_l(\xi)\, d\xi, \tag{3.63}$$

where

$$K_{ml}(x, \xi) = \sum_{\nu=0}^{N_l} b_{ml}^{(\nu)}(x) \frac{d^\nu}{dx^\nu} G_l(x, \xi) \tag{3.64}$$

$$(m, l = 1, 2, 3, \ldots).$$

If we apply the Sokolov method to the system of integral equations (3.63), that is, if we take as the nth approximation

$$v_{mn}(x) = f_m(x) + \lambda \sum_{l=1}^{\infty} \int_a^b K_{ml}(x, \xi) v_{ln-1}(\xi)\, d\xi$$
$$+ \lambda \sum_{l=1}^{N^*} \int_a^b K_{ml}(x, \xi) \alpha_{ln}^*(\xi)\, d\xi \qquad (m = 1, 2, 3, \ldots), \tag{3.65}$$

where

$$\alpha_{sn}^*(x) = \sum_{i=1}^{k_s} c_{ni}^{*(s)} \psi_{is}(x)$$
$$(s = 1, 2, \ldots, N^*; \quad i = 1, 2, \ldots, k_s), \tag{3.66}$$

$$\int_a^b \{\delta_{sn}^*(x) - \alpha_{sn}^*(x)\} \overline{\varphi_{sj}(x)}\, dx = 0$$
$$(j = 1, 2, \ldots, k_s), \tag{3.67}$$

$$\delta_{sn}^*(x) = v_{sn}(x) - v_{sn-1}(x),$$
$$v_{mo}(x) = g_m(x) \qquad (m, n = 1, 2, 3, \ldots) \tag{3.68}$$

and if we determine $\bar{y}_{mn}(x)$ from the problem

$$A_m \bar{y}_{mn}(x) = v_{mn}(x), \tag{3.69}$$

$$U_{m_r}(\bar{y}_{mn}) = 0 \qquad (r = 1, 2, \ldots, N_m), \tag{3.70}$$

then, on the basis of formulas (3.51), (3.53), (3.54), (3.58), (3.65), (3.66), (3.67), and (3.69), we can show that

$$\bar{y}_{mn}(x) = y_{mn}(x). \tag{3.71}$$

Therefore, the solution to the problem (3.69)–(3.70)—with note taken of (3.71)—takes the form

$$y_{mn}(x) = \int_a^b G_m(x, \xi) v_{mn}(\xi)\, d\xi. \tag{3.72}$$

Consequently, the question of the convergence of the sequences $y_{mn}(x)$, determined from the problem (3.51)–(3.52), reduces to the problem of convergence of the sequences $v_{mn}(x)$ given by (3.65) to the solution of the system of integral equations (3.63). This issue was examined in the preceding section. However, in calculating $\Lambda(\lambda)$ and $\Omega_m(\lambda)$ from formulas (3.30) and (3.32), we should bear in mind that the kernels $K_{ml}(x, \xi)$, have the form (3.64), that $N = \infty$, and that the functions $S_{sk_s}(x, \xi)$ are determined by the formulas

$$S_{sk_s}(x, \xi) = \sum_{i=1}^{k_s} \sum_{p=1}^{k_s} \mu_{pi}^{(s)} \psi_{si}(x) \overline{\varphi_{sp}(\xi)} \qquad (s = 1, 2, \dots, N^*),$$

$$\sum_{i=1}^{k_s} \mu_{pi}^{(s)} \gamma_{ij}^{(s)} = \delta_{jp} \qquad (p, j = 1, 2, \dots, k_s),$$

$$\gamma_{ij}^{(s)} = \int_a^b \psi_{si}(x) \overline{\varphi_{sj}(x)}\, dx.$$

By a procedure analogous to that used in Section 4 of Chapter I, we can, by virtue of (3.72), obtain the following error estimates:

$$|\Delta_{mn}(x)| \leqslant \frac{\bar{\varrho}_n \Omega_m(\lambda)}{1 - \Lambda(\lambda)} \bar{G}_m(x), \tag{3.73}$$

$$|\Delta_{mn}(x)| \leqslant \frac{\bar{\varrho}_1 \Omega_m(\lambda) \Lambda^{n-1}(\lambda)}{1 - \Lambda(\lambda)} \bar{G}_m(x), \tag{3.74}$$

where

$$\bar{G}_m(x) = \left\{ \int_a^b |G_m(x, \xi)|^q \, d\xi \right\}^{1/q},$$

$$\bar{\varrho}_n = \sup_l \left\{ \int_a^b |z_{ln}(\xi)|^p \, d\xi \right\}^{1/p} \qquad \text{[see the notation (3.21)]}$$

$$\Delta_{mn}(x) = y_m^*(x) - y_{mn}(x) \qquad (m, n = 1, 2, 3, \dots).$$

Example 13. Find the solution of the problem

$$y_m''(x) = \frac{ex^2 + 2x - x^2 - ex}{m(m+1)} - x^{m-1} + \sum_{l=1}^{\infty} \frac{x\{y_l'(x) - y_l(x)\}}{m(m+1)(l-1)!},$$

$$y_m(0) = y_m(1) = 0 \qquad (m = 1, 2, 3, \dots).$$

Suppose that

$$N^* = \infty, \qquad k_s = 1, \qquad \psi_{s1}(x) = -1, \qquad s = 1, 2, 3, \ldots.$$

Then, in accordance with (3.54)–(3.55),

$$\varphi_{s1}(x) = \tfrac{1}{2}x(1-x).$$

On the basis of formulas (3.51)–(3.53), we take as our first approximation

$$y''_{m1}(x) = \frac{ex^2 + 2x - x^2 - ex}{m(m+1)} - x^{m-1} + \sum_{l=1}^{\infty} \frac{x\{\alpha'_{l1}(x) - \alpha_{l1}(x)\}}{m(m+1)(l-1)!}, \tag{3.75}$$

$$\alpha_{m1}(x) = \frac{c_1^{(m)}}{2} x(1-x),$$

that is, we determine the first approximation from the problem

$$y''_{m1}(x) = \frac{ex^2 + 2x - x^2 - ex}{m(m+1)} - x^{m-1} + \sum_{l=1}^{\infty} \frac{c_1^{(l)}(x^3 - 3x^2 + x)}{2m(m+1)(l-1)!}, \tag{3.76}$$

$$y_{m1}(0) = y_{m1}(1) = 0 \qquad (m = 1, 2, 3, \ldots). \tag{3.77}$$

We determine the coefficient $c_1^{(m)}$ from the conditions

$$\int_0^1 \{y''_{m1}(x) - \alpha''_{m1}(x)\}x(1-x)\,dx = 0 \qquad (m = 1, 2, 3, \ldots). \tag{3.78}$$

If we substitute (3.76) and (3.75) in (3.78), we obtain the infinite system of algebraic equations

$$\frac{c_1^{(m)}}{6} = \frac{1}{(m+1)(m+2)} + \frac{2e-7}{60m(m+1)} + \sum_{l=1}^{\infty} \frac{c_1^{(l)}}{60m(m+1)(l-1)!},$$

from which we get

$$c_1^{(m)} = \frac{6}{(m+1)(m+2)} + \frac{11-4e}{(12-e)m(m+1)}.$$

Thus, when we solve the problem (3.76)–(3.77), we obtain as our first approximation

$$y_{m1}(x) = \frac{x(1-x^m)}{m(m+1)}$$
$$- \frac{0.0425x^5 - 0.0693x^4 + 0.0220x^3 + 0.0048x}{m(m+1)}.$$

By carrying out analogous calculations, we get as our second approximation

$$y_{m2}(x) = \frac{x(1-x^m)}{m(m+1)} + \frac{1}{m(m+1)}\{-0.0005x^8 + 0.0048x^7$$
$$- 0.0072x^6 + 0.0021x^5 + 0.0009x^4 - 0.0002x^3$$
$$+ 0.0001x\}.$$

The errors in the first and second approximations for $x = 0.5$ do not exceed 0.88 and 0.016%, respectively.

In this example, the sufficient condition of the form (3.34) for convergence of the method of successive approximations is not satisfied.

Note 1. The method we have been illustrating can be applied to differential equations of a more complicated form than (3.47) and under weaker restrictions imposed on the coefficients and the free terms. For example, we may assume their summability on the interval $[a, b]$. Also, the boundary conditions may be inhomogeneous and of a more general form than (3.48). Finally, the interval $[a, b]$ may be infinite.

Note 2. Everything that has been said in the present section can be carried over without significant changes to systems of integrodifferential equations of the form

$$A_m[x, y_m(x)] = f_m(x) + \lambda \sum_{l=1}^{N} B_{ml}[x, y_l(x)]$$

$$(m = 1, 2, \ldots, N),$$

where

$$A_m[x, y_m(x)] = \sum_{\nu=0}^{N_m} \alpha_{m\nu}(x) y_m^{(\nu)}(x)$$
$$+ \int_a^b \sum_{\nu=0}^{N_m-1} K_{m\nu}(x, \xi) y_m^{(\nu)}(\xi)\, d\xi$$
$$+ \int_a^x \sum_{\nu=0}^{N_m-1} H_{m\nu}(x, \xi) y_m^{(\nu)}(\xi)\, d\xi,$$

$$B_{ml}[x, y_l(x)] = \sum_{\nu=0}^{N_l^*} b_{ml\nu}(x) y_l^{(\nu)}(x)$$
$$+ \int_a^b \sum_{\nu=0}^{N_l^*-1} M_{ml\nu}(x, \xi) y_l^{(\nu)}(\xi)\, d\xi$$
$$+ \int_a^x \sum_{\nu=0}^{N_l^*-1} \Gamma_{ml\nu}(x, \xi) y_l^{(\nu)}(\xi)\, d\xi.$$

Here, $N_m > N_l^*$ for arbitrary fixed $m = l$ (where $l = 1, 2, 3, \ldots N$), N is finite or infinite, and $a \leqslant x \leqslant b$. With regard to the operator $A_m[x, y_m(x)]$, we require that the problem

$$A_m[x, w_m(x)] = 0,$$

$$U_{m_r}(w_m) = 0 \qquad (r = 1, 2, \ldots, N_m)$$

have only the trivial solution and that it be possible to express Green's function $G_m(x, \xi)$ in explicit form.

CHAPTER **IV**

Application of the Method to Systems of Linear Algebraic Equations

1. Infinite Systems of Linear Algebraic Equations in the Space l^p

1. In the present section, the Sokolov method will be used to find the solution of an infinite system of linear algebraic equations

$$x_m = b_m + \lambda \sum_{l=1}^{\infty} a_{ml} x_l \qquad (m = 1, 2, 3, \ldots) \tag{4.1}$$

under the assumption that the free terms b_m and the coefficients a_{ml} satisfy the conditions

$$\sum_{m=1}^{\infty} |b_m|^p < \infty, \qquad \sum_{m=1}^{\infty} \left\{ \sum_{l=1}^{\infty} |\lambda a_{ml}|^\gamma \right\}^{p/q} < \infty, \tag{4.2}$$

where

$$\frac{1}{p} + \frac{1}{q} = 1 \qquad (1 < p < \infty, \qquad 1 < q < \infty).$$

In the case in which $p = 1$ and $q = \infty$, we assume

$$\sum_{m=1}^{\infty} |b_m| < \infty, \qquad \sum_{m=1}^{\infty} \sup_l |\lambda a_{ml}| < \infty, \tag{4.3}$$

and in the case in which $p = \infty$ and $q = 1$,

$$\sup_m |b_m| < \infty, \qquad \sup_m \sum_{l=1}^{\infty} |\lambda a_{ml}| < \infty. \tag{4.4}$$

The essence of the method consists in the following. As our first approximation, we take

$$x_{m1} = b_m + \lambda \sum_{l=1}^{k} a_{ml} x_{l1} + \lambda \sum_{l=k+1}^{\infty} a_{ml} x_{l0} \qquad (4.5)$$

$$(m = 1, 2, 3, \ldots),$$

where

$$x_0 = \{x_{10}, x_{20}, \ldots, x_{m0}, \ldots\}$$

is an arbitrary element of the space l^p.

From the finite system of equations

$$x_{m1} = b_m + \lambda \sum_{l=1}^{k} a_{ml} x_{l1} + \lambda \sum_{l=k+1}^{\infty} a_{ml} x_{l0}$$

$$(m = 1, 2, \ldots, k)$$

we find x_{ml}

$$x_{m1} = \sum_{i=1}^{k} \frac{M_{im}(\lambda)}{D_k(\lambda)} \left\{ b_i + \lambda \sum_{l=k+1}^{\infty} a_{il} x_{l0} \right\} \qquad (4.6)$$

$$(m = 1, 2, \ldots, k)$$

where

$$D_k(\lambda) = \begin{vmatrix} 1 - \lambda a_{11} & \cdots & -\lambda a_{1k} \\ \cdots & \cdots & \cdots \\ -\lambda a_{k1} & \cdots & 1 - \lambda a_{kk} \end{vmatrix},$$

and $M_{ij}(\lambda)$ is the cofactor of the element in the ith row and jth column.

When we substitute these values of x_{ml} (for $m = 1, 2, \ldots, k$) in the right-hand side of (4.5), we obtain

$$x_{m1} = b_m + \lambda \sum_{l=k+1}^{\infty} a_{ml} x_{l0} + \lambda \sum_{i=1}^{k} \sum_{j=1}^{k} \frac{M_{ij}(\lambda)}{D_k(\lambda)} a_{mj} b_i$$

$$+ \lambda^2 \sum_{l=k+1}^{\infty} \sum_{i=1}^{k} \sum_{j=1}^{k} \frac{M_{ij}(\lambda)}{D_k(\lambda)} a_{il} a_{mj} x_{l0},$$

or

$$x_{m1} = g_{k,m} + \sum_{l=k+1}^{\infty} L_{k,ml}(\lambda) x_{l0} \qquad (m = 1, 2, 3, \ldots), \quad (4.7)$$

where

$$g_{k,m} = b_m + \lambda \sum_{i=1}^{k} \sum_{j=1}^{k} \frac{M_{ij}(\lambda)}{D_k(\lambda)} a_{mj} b_i, \tag{4.8}$$

$$L_{k,ml}(\lambda) = \lambda a_{ml} + \lambda^2 \sum_{i=1}^{k} \sum_{j=1}^{k} \frac{M_{ij}(\lambda)}{D_k(\lambda)} a_{mj} a_{il}$$

$$(m, l = 1, 2, 3, \ldots). \tag{4.9}$$

For our nth approximation, we put

$$x_{mn} = b_m + \lambda \sum_{l=1}^{k} a_{ml} x_{ln} + \lambda \sum_{l=k+1}^{\infty} a_{ml} x_{ln-1} \tag{4.10}$$

$$(m = 1, 2, 3, \ldots).$$

In analogy with the above, from the finite system of equations

$$x_{mn} = b_m + \lambda \sum_{l=1}^{k} a_{ml} x_{ln} + \lambda \sum_{l=k+1}^{\infty} a_{ml} x_{ln-1}$$

$$(m = 1, 2, 3, \ldots, k)$$

we find x_{mn}:

$$x_{mn} = \sum_{i=1}^{k} \frac{M_{im}(\lambda)}{D_k(\lambda)} \left\{ b_i + \lambda \sum_{l=k+1}^{\infty} a_{il} x_{ln-1} \right\} \tag{4.11}$$

$$(m = 1, 2, \ldots, k).$$

When we substitute (4.11) in the right-hand side of (4.10), we obtain

$$x_{mn} = g_{k,m} + \sum_{l=k+1}^{\infty} L_{k,ml}(\lambda) x_{ln-1} \tag{4.12}$$

$$(m = 1, 2, \ldots).$$

From formula (4.12), it is easy to obtain a sufficient condition for convergence of the sequence x_{mn}. Specifically, on the basis of (4.12),

$$x_{mn} - x_{mn-1} = \sum_{l=k+1}^{\infty} L_{k,ml}(\lambda)(x_{ln-1} - x_{ln-2})$$

$$(m = 1, 2, 3, \ldots),$$

so that, by using Hölder's inequality,

$$|x_{mn} - x_{mn-1}| \leqslant \Omega_{km}(\lambda)\left\{\sum_{l=k+1}^{\infty} |x_{ln-1} - x_{ln-2}|^p\right\}^{1/p}, \quad (4.13)$$

$$\Omega_{km}(\lambda) = \left\{\sum_{l=k+1}^{\infty} |L_{k,ml}(\lambda)|^q\right\}^{1/q}. \quad (4.14)$$

When we take the pth power of (4.13) and sum the result over m from $k + 1$ to ∞, we obtain

$$\left\{\sum_{m=k+1}^{\infty} |x_{mn} - x_{mn-1}|^p\right\}^{1/p} \leqslant L_k(\lambda)\left\{\sum_{l=k+1}^{\infty} |x_{ln-1} - x_{ln-2}|^p\right\}^{1/p}$$

$$\leqslant L_k^{n-1}(\lambda)\left\{\sum_{l=k+1}^{\infty} |x_{l1} - x_{l0}|^p\right\}^{1/p}, \quad (4.15)$$

where

$$L_k(\lambda) = \left\{\sum_{m=k+1}^{\infty}\left[\sum_{l=k+1}^{\infty} |L_{k,ml}(\lambda)|^q\right]^{p/q}\right\}^{1/p}. \quad (4.16)$$

When we substitute (4.15) into (4.13), we finally obtain

$$|x_{mn} - x_{mn-1}| \leqslant \Omega_{km}(\lambda)L_k^{n-2}(\lambda)\left\{\sum_{l=k+1}^{\infty} |x_{l1} - x_{l0}|^p\right\}^{1/p}. \quad (4.17)$$

It is clear from (4.17) that if $L_k(\lambda) < 1$, the sequence (4.12) converges to the limit $x_m{}^*$, where

$$x^* = \{x_1{}^*, x_2{}^*, \ldots, x_m{}^*, \ldots\} \in l^p.$$

If we pass to the limit in Eq. (4.10), we see immediately that the system of numbers $x_m{}^*$ is a solution of Eqs. (4.1).

By using the results of Section 3 of Chapter I, we can show that $L_k(\lambda) \to 0$ as $k \to \infty$ and that $L_k(\lambda)^* \geqslant 1$ for an arbitrary eigenvalue λ^*. From this it follows that in the case of a regular value of λ, we can always choose a finite value of k so that $L_k(\lambda) < 1$.

We note that when $p = 1$ and $q = \infty$, and when $p = \infty$ and

$q = 1$, sufficient conditions for convergence of the sequence (4.12) are, respectively, as follows:

$$L_k(\lambda) = \sum_{m=k+1}^{\infty} \sup_{l>k} |L_{k,ml}(\lambda)| < 1, \tag{4.18}$$

$$L_k(\lambda) = \sup_{m>k} \sum_{l=k+1}^{\infty} |L_{k,ml}(\lambda)| < 1. \tag{4.18*}$$

Suppose that $x_m{}^*$ and x_{mn} are, respectively, the exact and the approximate solution of Eq. (4.1). Then, by a procedure analogous to that used in Section 4 of Chapter I, we may obtain the following error estimates:

$$|x_m{}^* - x_{mn}| \leqslant \frac{\Omega_{km}(\lambda)}{1 - L_k(\lambda)} \left\{ \sum_{l=k+1}^{\infty} |x_{ln} - x_{ln-1}|^p \right\}^{1/p}, \tag{4.19}$$

$$|x_m{}^* - x_{mn}| \leqslant \frac{\Omega_{km}(\lambda) L_k^{n-1}(\lambda)}{1 - L_k(\lambda)} \left\{ \sum_{l=k+1}^{\infty} |x_{l1} - x_{l0}|^p \right\}^{1/p}, \tag{4.20}$$

$$I_{mn} = \frac{|x_m{}^* - x_{mn}|}{|x_m{}^*|} \leqslant \frac{100 |x_m{}^* - x_{mn}| \,\%}{|x_{mn}| - |x_m{}^* - x_{mn}|} \quad (n \geqslant n_0). \tag{4.21}$$

Example 14. Find x_m from the system of equations

$$x_m = \frac{32}{2^m} - 5 \sum_{l=1}^{\infty} \frac{x_l}{2^{m+l}} \qquad \left(x_m{}^* = \frac{12}{2^m} \right).$$

On the basis of formulas (4.8) and (4.9) we have, for $k = 2$,

$$g_{2,m} = \frac{512}{41} \cdot \frac{1}{2^m}, \qquad L_{2,ml}(-5) = -\frac{80}{41} \cdot \frac{1}{2^{m+l}}.$$

Therefore, from formula (4.12),

$$x_{mn} = \frac{512}{41} \cdot \frac{1}{2^m} - \frac{80}{41} \sum_{l=3}^{\infty} \frac{x_{ln-1}}{2^{m+l}} \qquad (m = 1, 2, 3, \ldots).$$

If $x_{10} = x_{20} = \cdots = x_{m0} = \cdots = 0$, then

$$x_{mn} = \frac{12}{2^m} \left\{ 1 + (-1)^{n-1} \cdot \frac{5^n}{123^n} \right\}.$$

In the present example [see formulas (4.14) and (4.16)],

$$L_2(-5) = \frac{5}{123}, \qquad \Omega_{2m}(-5) = \frac{20\sqrt{3}}{123} \cdot \frac{1}{2^m}.$$

If we carry out the calculations for the error estimate by using formula (4.19), we obtain

$$|x_m{}^* - x_{mn}| \leqslant \frac{64}{59} \cdot \frac{5^n}{123^n} \cdot \frac{12}{2^m}.$$

The exact value is

$$|x_m{}^* - x_{mn}| = \frac{5^n}{123^n} \cdot \frac{12}{2^m}.$$

When we compare the error estimate that we have obtained with the exact one, we note that the deviation does not exceed 8.5% for any value of m or n.

In the present example, the estimate obtained by use of formula (4.20) coincides with that obtained by use of formula (4.19).

According to formula (4.21),

$$I_{m1} \leqslant 4.425\,\%; \qquad I_{m2} \leqslant 0.180\,\%; \qquad I_{m3} \leqslant 0.0073\,\%;$$

The exact values are

$$I_{m1} = 4.065\,\%; \qquad I_{m2} = 0.165\,\%, \qquad I_{m3} = 0.0067\,\%$$

uniformly with respect to m.

In general, for the equation

$$x_m = b_m + \lambda \sum_{l=1}^{\infty} \frac{x_l}{2^{m+l}},$$

for which $\lambda = 3$ is an eigenvalue, we obtain, according to (4.9) and (4.16),

$$L_{0,ml}(\lambda) = \frac{\lambda}{2^{m+l}}, \qquad L_{1,ml}(\lambda) = \frac{4\lambda}{4-\lambda} \cdot \frac{1}{2^{m+l}},$$

$$L_{2,ml}(\lambda) = \frac{16\lambda}{16-5\lambda} \cdot \frac{1}{2^{m+l}},$$

$$L_0{}^2(\lambda) = \frac{\lambda^2}{9}, \qquad L_1{}^2(\lambda) = \frac{\lambda^2}{9(4-\lambda)^2},$$

$$L_2{}^2(\lambda) = \frac{\lambda^2}{9(16-5\lambda)^2};$$

$$L_0(3) = L_1(3) = L_2(3) = 1.$$

From the sufficient condition $L_k(\lambda) < 1$ for the convergence of the Sokolov method, which in the present example is also necessary, it follows that this method diverges only in the closed intervals [3, 6] and $[3, 3\frac{3}{7}]$ for $k = 1$ and $k = 2$, respectively, whereas the method of successive approximations converges only in the open interval $(-3, 3)$.

2. Let us suppose that the conditions (4.2) or (4.3) and (4.4) are satisfied, and

$$D(\lambda) = \lim_{k \to \infty} D_k(\lambda) \neq 0, \tag{4.22}$$

and let us express successively the first k unknowns $x_1, x_2, \ldots, x_k$ in terms of $x_{k+1}, x_{k+2} \ldots$ either singly or in groups. Then, as was shown in [40], we obtain the system

$$x_m = g_{k,m} + \sum_{l=k+1}^{\infty} L_{k,ml}(\lambda) x_l \qquad (m = 1, 2, 3, \ldots). \tag{4.23}$$

If we disregard the first k equations of the system (4.23), we obtain the following infinite system:

$$x_m = g_{k,m} + \sum_{l=k+1}^{\infty} L_{k,ml}(\lambda) x_1 \qquad (m = k+1, k+2, \ldots). \tag{4.24}$$

Since $L_k(\lambda) \to 0$ as $k \to \infty$, we have the following theorem.

THEOREM 14. *If we express successively the first unknowns in the system* (4.1) *whose coefficients and right-hand members satisfy conditions* (4.2) *and* (4.22), *in terms of the remaining unknowns, we shall always arrive at a system of the form* (4.24), *which can be solved by the method of successive approximations. Then, after the* $(n-1)$*st iteration and substitution of the result obtained into* (4.23), *we obtain formula* (4.12).

Example 15. The system of equations

$$x_m = 1 - \frac{e}{m} + \sum_{l=1}^{\infty} \frac{x_l}{m(l-1)!} \qquad (m = 1, 2, 3, \ldots) \tag{4.25}$$

has the solution $x_m = 1$.

For the present system, condition (4.4) is satisfied.

We cannot apply the method of successive approximations to the system (4.25) since

$$L_0(1) = \sup_{m>0} \sum_{l=1}^{\infty} \left| \frac{1}{m(l-1)!} \right| = \sum_{l=1}^{\infty} \frac{1}{(l-1)!} = e > 1,$$

and $D_1(1) = 0$. Therefore, we determine from the system (4.25) at one time two unknowns x_1 and x_2:

$$x_1 = 2e - 3 - 2\sum_{l=3}^{\infty} \frac{x_l}{(l-1)!}; \qquad x_2 = e - 1 - \sum_{l=3}^{\infty} \frac{x_l}{(l-1)!}. \tag{4.26}$$

When we substitute these values in the right-hand sides of (4.25), we obtain

$$x_m = 1 + \frac{2e-4}{m} - \sum_{l=3}^{\infty} \frac{2x_l}{m(l-1)!} \qquad (m = 1, 2, 3, \ldots). \tag{4.27}$$

$$L_2(1) = \sup_{m>2} \sum_{l=3}^{\infty} \left| \frac{1}{m(l-1)!} \right| = \frac{2}{3}(e-2) \approx 0.47885.$$

We can now apply the method of successive approximations to the system (4.27), but, in order to improve the convergence, let us eliminate one more unknown x_3. From the third equation of the system (4.27), we have

$$x_3 = \frac{e}{2} - \frac{1}{4} - \sum_{l=4}^{\infty} \frac{x_l}{2(l-1)!}. \tag{4.28}$$

When we substitute this value in the right-hand members of (4.27), we obtain

$$x_m = 1 + \frac{6e-15}{4m} - \sum_{l=4}^{\infty} \frac{3x_l}{2m(l-1)!} \qquad (m = 1, 2, 3, \ldots), \tag{4.29}$$

$$L_3(1) = \sup_{m>3} \sum_{l=4}^{\infty} \left| \frac{3}{2m(l-1)!} \right| = \frac{3}{8}(e-2.5) \approx 0.08186.$$

If we take as our zeroth approximation $x_{m0} = 1 + (6e - 15)/4m$, the $(n - 1)$st iteration, when applied to the system

$$x_m = 1 + \frac{6e - 15}{4m} - \sum_{l=4}^{\infty} \frac{3x_l}{2m(l-1)!} \qquad (m = 4, 5, \ldots),$$

yields

$$x_{mn-1} = 1 + (-1)^{n-1} \cdot \frac{6e - 15}{4m} \left(\frac{3e - 8}{2}\right)^{n-1} \qquad (m = 4, 5, \ldots). \tag{4.30}$$

When we substitute (4.30) in the right-hand members of (4.29), we obtain the nth approximate solution for the system (4.25):

$$x_{mn} = 1 + (-1)^n \cdot \frac{6e - 15}{4m} \cdot \left(\frac{3e - 8}{2}\right)^n$$

$$(n = 0, 1, 2, \ldots; \quad m = 1, 2, 3, \ldots).$$

On the basis of (4.19)

$$|x_m{}^* - x_{mn}| \leqslant 1.241 \cdot \frac{6e - 15}{4m} \cdot \left(\frac{3e - 8}{2}\right)^n.$$

The exact value is

$$|x_m{}^* - x_{mn}| = \frac{6e - 15}{4m} \cdot \left(\frac{3e - 8}{2}\right)^n.$$

From this, it is clear that the difference $|x_m{}^* - x_{mn}|$ between the estimated and exact values does not exceed 24.1% for any value of m or n.

2. Finite Systems of Linear Algebraic Equations

In solving many problems encountered in physics and technology, we obtain systems of linear algebraic equations. Such systems are also of great significance in the solution of linear differential, integral, and integrodifferential equations. For example, in the solution of such equations by familiar methods (Galerkin's, Ritz', moments, nets, least squares, etc.), we find it necessary to solve finite systems of equations.

The question of the solution of such systems is quite old. However, even today a large number of new books and papers are devoted to it, and, as yet, there is no consensus as to which of the existing methods is the best. For a detailed study of this question, the reader should refer to the current literature (see, for example, [2, 4, 65]) and the bibliography in [58], in which more than 450 references are included.

The classical methods of solving systems of equations, for example, Gauss' method and the method of solution by means of determinants, are giving way to iterative methods of approximation. The simplest of these are the method of successive approximations and the Seidel method.

The basic principle involved in the method of successive approximations was given in the introduction. The Seidel method consists in starting with an arbitrary vector

$$x_0 = \{x_{10}, x_{20}, \ldots, x_{N0}\}$$

and getting approximate solutions $x_n = \{x_{1n}, x_{2n}, \ldots, x_{Nn}\}$ of the system of equations

$$x_m = b_m + \lambda \sum_{l=1}^{N} a_{ml} x_l \qquad (m = 1, 2, \ldots, N) \tag{4.31}$$

as follows:

$$x_{mn} = b_m + \lambda \sum_{l=1}^{m-1} a_{ml} x_{ln} + \lambda \sum_{l=m}^{N} a_{ml} x_{ln-1}.$$

A defect in the method of successive approximations and the Seidel method lies in the fact that they can be successfully applied only to systems of a definite type.

1. Let us solve the system of equations (4.31) by Sokolov's method. Using this method we start with an arbitrary initial approximation $x_0 = \{x_{10}, x_{20}, \ldots, x_{N0}\}$, and determine the successive approximations as follows:

$$x_{mn} = b_m + \lambda \sum_{l=1}^{N} a_{ml} x_{ln-1} + \lambda \sum_{l=1}^{k} C_{mi} \alpha_{in} \tag{4.32}$$

$$(m = 1, 2, \ldots, N; \quad n = 1, 2, 3, \ldots),$$

where

$$C_{mi} = (a_m, \varphi_i) = \sum_{l=1}^{N} a_{ml}\varphi_{il}, \tag{4.33}$$

$$a_m = \{a_{m1}, a_{m2}, \ldots, a_{mN}\}; \quad \varphi_i = \{\varphi_{i1}, \varphi_{i2}, \ldots, \varphi_{iN}\}$$

($i = 1, 2, \ldots, k$ and $k \leqslant N$) is a system of orthogonal vectors.

The parameters α_{in} are determined from the conditions

$$\alpha_{in} = \frac{(\delta_n, \varphi_i)}{(\varphi_i, \varphi_i)} = \frac{1}{\gamma_i} \sum_{m=1}^{N} \delta_{mn}\varphi_{im}, \tag{4.34}$$

$$\gamma_i = (\varphi_i, \varphi_i) \qquad (i = 1, 2, \ldots, k),$$

$$\delta_{mn} = x_{mn} - x_{mn-1}. \tag{4.35}$$

On the basis of formulas (4.32), (4.34), and (4.35), the α_{in} are determined from the system

$$\alpha_{in} = f_{in-1} + \lambda \sum_{j=1}^{k} g_{ij}\alpha_{jn}, \tag{4.36}$$

where

$$g_{ij} = \frac{1}{\gamma_i} \sum_{m=1}^{N} C_{mj}\varphi_{im}, \qquad f_{in-1} = \frac{1}{\gamma_i} \sum_{m=1}^{N} \varepsilon_{mn-1}\varphi_{im},$$

$$\varepsilon_{mn-1} = b_m - x_{mn-1} + \lambda \sum_{l=1}^{N} a_{ml}x_{ln-1}.$$

If we determine α_{in} from the system (4.36) and substitute the value obtained in (4.32), we finally obtain the nth approximation.

Since the conditions for the convergence of the sequence (4.32) to the solution of the system (4.31) are studied in the first chapter, there is no need to discuss them in detail at this point. We give only the sufficient condition for convergence:

$$L_k(\lambda) = \left\{ \sum_{m=1}^{N} \sum_{l=1}^{N} |L_{ml}^{(k)}(\lambda)|^2 \right\}^{1/2} < 1, \tag{4.37}$$

where

$$L_{ml}^{(k)}(\lambda) = \Omega_{ml}^{(k)}(\lambda) - \sum_{p=1}^{k} W_{pl}^{(k)} \varphi_{pm}, \tag{4.38}$$

$$W_{pl}^{(k)} = \frac{1}{\gamma_p} \sum_{m=1}^{N} \varphi_{pm} \Omega_{ml}^{(k)}(\lambda),$$

$$\begin{aligned}\Omega_{ml}^{(k)}(\lambda) &= \lambda\left\{a_{ml} - \sum_{i=1}^{k} \frac{C_{mi}}{\gamma_i} \varphi_{il}\right\} \\ &+ \lambda^2 \sum_{i=1}^{k} \sum_{j=1}^{k} C_{mj} \mu_{ij}(\lambda) \cdot \frac{1}{\gamma_i} \sum_{v=1}^{N} \varphi_{iv}\left\{a_{vl} - \sum_{s=1}^{k} \frac{C_{vs}}{\gamma_s} \varphi_{sl}\right\},\end{aligned} \tag{4.39}$$

$$\mu_{ij}(\lambda) = \frac{M_{ij}(\lambda)}{D_k(\lambda)}, \qquad D_k(\lambda) = \begin{vmatrix} 1 - \lambda g_{11} & \cdots & -\lambda g_{1k} \\ \cdots & \cdots & \cdots \\ -\lambda g_{k1} & \cdots & 1 - \lambda g_{kk} \end{vmatrix}$$

and $M_{ij}(\lambda)$ is the cofactor of the element in the ith row in jth column.

If $k = 0$ or if all the $C_{mi} = 0$, the sequence (4.32) takes the form

$$\tilde{x}_{mn} = b_m + \lambda \sum_{l=1}^{N} a_{ml} \tilde{x}_{ln-1}.$$

From this it is clear that $\tilde{x}_{nm}$ represents the nth approximate solution of the system (4.31) obtained by the usual method of successive approximations. In this case, we obtain from (4.37) the familiar sufficient condition for convergence of the method of successive approximations

$$L_0(\lambda) = \left\{\sum_{m=1}^{N} \sum_{l=1}^{N} |\lambda a_{ml}|^2\right\}^{1/2} < 1. \tag{4.40}$$

On the basis of Theorem 6, we may conclude that the inequality $L_{k_1}(\lambda) < 1$, implies the inequality $L_{k_2}(\lambda) < 1$ for arbitrary k_1 and k_2 satisfying the condition that $k_1 < k_2 \leqslant N$, and $L_{k_2}(\lambda) \leqslant L_{k_1}(\lambda)$. In particular, if $L_0(\lambda) < 1$, the Sokolov method converges for an arbitrary choice of $k \leqslant N$. When the matrix $[a_{ml}]$ is Hermitian and λ is a real number, convergence by the method of successive approximations always implies convergence of the Sokolov method.

Suppose that $x_m{}^*$ and x_{mn} are, respectively, the exact and the approximate solutions of the system (4.31). Then we have the following error estimates:

$$|x_m{}^* - x_{mn}| \leqslant \frac{\varrho_{nk}}{1 - L_s(\lambda)} \Omega_{sm}(\lambda), \tag{4.41}$$

$$|x_m{}^* - x_{mn}| \leqslant \frac{\varrho_{1k} L_s^{n-1}(\lambda)}{1 - L_s(\lambda)} \Omega_{sm}(\lambda) \qquad (0 \leqslant s \leqslant k), \tag{4.42}$$

where

$$\Omega_{sm}(\lambda) = \left\{ \sum_{l=1}^{N} |\Omega_{ml}^{(s)}(\lambda)|^2 \right\}^{1/2}, \tag{4.43}$$

$$\varrho_{nk} = \left\{ \sum_{l=1}^{N} \left| \delta_{ln} - \sum_{i=1}^{k} \alpha_{in} \varphi_{il} \right|^2 \right\}^{1/2}. \tag{4.44}$$

Note 1. In practice, it is more convenient to use the following sufficient condition for convergence of the method:

$$L_k(\lambda) = \max_m \sum_{l=1}^{N} |L_{ml}^{(k)}(\lambda)| < 1.$$

However, with such a norm, we cannot conclude that $L_{k_1}(\lambda) < 1$, implies $L_{k_2}(\lambda) < 1$ for an arbitrary k_2 (where $k_1 < k_2 \leqslant N$). Here

$$\Omega_{sm}(\lambda) = \sum_{l=1}^{N} |\Omega_{ml}^{(s)}(\lambda)|,$$

$$\varrho_{nk} = \max_m \left| \delta_{mn} - \sum_{i=1}^{k} \alpha_{in} \varphi_{im} \right|.$$

Example 16. The integral equation

$$y(x) = 3 - (x + 16) \ln \sqrt[5]{(x + 16)} + (x + 6) \ln \sqrt[5]{(x + 6)} + \int_0^{10} \ln \sqrt[5]{(x + \xi + 6)}\, y(\xi)\, d\xi \tag{4.45}$$

has the very simple solution $y(x) = 1$.

By applying the method of replacing the integral equation with a finite system of linear algebraic equations, we obtain

$$\bar{y}(x) = 3 - (x + 16) \ln \sqrt[5]{(x + 16)} + (x + 6) \ln \sqrt[5]{(x + 6)} + \sum_{m=1}^{5} 2 \ln \sqrt[5]{(x + 5 + 2m)}\, x_m,$$

where

$$x_m = \bar{y}(2m - 1) \qquad (m = 1, 2, 3, 4, 5).$$

For determining x_i we have the following system of equations:

$$x_1 = -3.90864 + 0.83178x_1 + 0.92104x_2 + 0.99396x_3 + 1.05562x_4 + 1.10904x_5,$$

$$x_2 = -4.23388 + 0.92104x_1 + 0.99396x_2 + 1.05562x_3 + 1.10904x_4 + 1.15615x_5,$$

$$x_3 = -4.51160 + 0.99396x_1 + 1.05562x_2 + 1.10904x_3 + 1.15615x_4 + 1.19829x_5,$$

$$x_4 = -4.75438 + 1.05562x_1 + 1.10904x_2 + 1.15615x_3 + 1.19829x_4 + 1.23642x_5,$$

$$x_5 = -4.97025 + 1.10904x_1 + 1.15615x_2 + 1.19829x_3 + 1.23642x_4 + 1.27122x_5.$$

Suppose that $k = 1$, that $\varphi_1 = \{1, 1, 1, 1, 1\}$ and that $x_0 = \{0, 0, 0, 0, 0\}$. Then, in accordance with (4.32) and (4.33), we have as our first approximation

$$x_{11} = -3.90864 + 4.91144\alpha_1,$$

$$x_{21} = -4.23388 + 5.23581\alpha_1,$$

$$x_{31} = -4.51160 + 5.51306\alpha_1,$$

$$x_{41} = -4.75438 + 5.75552\alpha_1,$$

$$x_{51} = -4.97025 + 5.97112\alpha_1.$$

On the basis of (4.34),

$$\alpha_1 = \tfrac{1}{5}(x_{11} + x_{21} + x_{31} + x_{41} + x_{51}).$$

Consequently, we obtain the equation

$$4.47739\alpha_1 = 4.47575,$$

for determining α_1, from which we get

$$\alpha_1 = 0.99963.$$

Thus,

$$x_{11} = 1.00100, \qquad x_{21} = 1.00001, \qquad x_{31} = 0.99944,$$
$$x_{41} = 0.99903, \qquad x_{51} = 0.99868.$$

As our second approximation, we obtain

$$\begin{aligned} x_{12} &= 1.00060 + 4.91144\alpha_2, \\ x_{22} &= 0.99967 + 5.23581\alpha_2, \\ x_{32} &= 0.99914 + 5.51306\alpha_2, \\ x_{42} &= 0.99876 + 5.75552\alpha_2, \\ x_{52} &= 0.99844 + 5.97112\alpha_2, \end{aligned}$$

$$\alpha_2 = \tfrac{1}{5}(x_{12} - x_{11} + x_{22} - x_{21} + x_{32} - x_{31} + x_{42} - x_{41} + x_{52} - x_{51}),$$

$$\alpha_2 = -0.00031 + 5.47739\alpha_2,$$

$$\alpha_2 = 0.000069.$$

$$x_{12} = 1.00094, \qquad x_{22} = 1.00003, \qquad x_{32} = 0.99952,$$
$$x_{42} = 0.99916, \qquad x_{52} = 0.99885.$$

On the basis of formulas (4.37) and (4.43), we have

$$L_1(1) = 0.10326; \qquad \Omega_{11}(1) = 0.03561; \qquad \Omega_{12}(1) = 0.01009;$$
$$\Omega_{13}(1) = 0.04473; \qquad \Omega_{14}(1) = 0.07242; \qquad \Omega_{15}(1) = 0.09520.$$

Therefore, in accordance with (4.41) and (4.21), we have, for $s = 1$,

$$|x_1{}^* - x_{11}| \leqslant 0.00007; \qquad |x_2{}^* - x_{21}| \leqslant 0.00002;$$
$$|x_3{}^* - x_{31}| \leqslant 0.00009;$$
$$|x_4{}^* - x_{41}| \leqslant 0.00014; \qquad |x_5{}^* - x_{51}| \leqslant 0.00019;$$
$$I_{11} \leqslant 0.007\,\%; \qquad I_{21} \leqslant 0.002\,\%;$$
$$I_{31} \leqslant 0.009\,\%;$$
$$I_{41} \leqslant 0.014\,\%; \qquad I_{51} \leqslant 0.019\,\%.$$

Note 2. The parameters α_{in} appearing in formulas (4.32) can also be determined from the conditions

$$(\alpha_n - \delta_n, \psi_i) = 0 \qquad (i = 1, 2, \ldots, k) \tag{4.46}$$

or from the condition

$$(\alpha_n - \delta_n, \alpha_n - \delta_n) = \min, \tag{4.47}$$

where

$$\alpha_n = \sum_{i=1}^{k} \alpha_{in}\varphi_i,$$

$$\delta_n = \{\delta_{1n}, \delta_{2n}, \ldots, \delta_{Nn}\},$$

and $\varphi_i = \{\varphi_{1i}, \varphi_{2i}, \ldots, \varphi_{Ni}\}$ and $\psi_i = \{\psi_{1i}, \psi_{2i}, \ldots, \psi_{Ni}\}$ are systems of linearly independent vectors.

Example 17. Let us solve the system

$$\begin{aligned} x_1 &= 0.76 + 0.22x_1 + 0.02x_2 + 0.12x_3 + 0.14x_4; \\ x_2 &= 0.08 + 0.02x_1 + 0.14x_2 + 0.04x_3 - 0.06x_4; \\ x_3 &= 1.12 + 0.12x_1 + 0.04x_2 + 0.28x_3 + 0.08x_4; \\ x_4 &= 0.68 + 0.14x_1 - 0.06x_2 + 0.08x_3 + 0.26x_4 \end{aligned} \tag{4.48}$$

by the method of iteration. (This system is taken from [2], p. 446.)

If we take as our zeroth approximation the vector {0.76, 0.08, 1.12, 0.68}, the eighth approximation by the method of successive approximations yields:

$$\tilde{x}_{18} = 1.532746; \qquad \tilde{x}_{28} = 0.122009;$$

$$\tilde{x}_{38} = 1.972937; \qquad \tilde{x}_{48} = 1.410737.$$

The exact solution of the system (4.48) correct to the sixth decimal place is

$$x_1 = 1.534965; \qquad x_2 = 0.122010;$$

$$x_3 = 1.975156; \qquad x_4 = 1.412955.$$

The absolute error for the eighth approximation of these values is, respectively, 0.002219, 0.000001, 0.002219, and 0.002218.

Let us solve the system (4.48) by the Sokolov method by taking as the coordinate function $\varphi_1 = \{1, 0, 1, 1\}$, which is an eigenvector of the matrix

$$\begin{bmatrix} 0.22 & 0.02 & 0.12 & 0.14 \\ 0.02 & 0.14 & 0.04 & -0.06 \\ 0.12 & 0.04 & 0.28 & 0.08 \\ 0.14 & -0.06 & 0.08 & 0.26 \end{bmatrix}. \tag{4.49}$$

As our zeroth approximation, we take

$$\begin{aligned} x_{10} &= 0.76 + 0.48\alpha_0 ; \\ x_{20} &= 0.08; \\ x_{30} &= 1.12 + 0.48\alpha_0 ; \\ x_{40} &= 0.68 + 0.48\alpha_0 , \end{aligned} \tag{4.50}$$

where 0.48 is an eigenvalue of the matrix (4.49) and the parameter α_0 is determined in accordance with formula (4.34), that is,

$$\alpha_0 = \tfrac{1}{3}(x_{10} + x_{30} + x_{40}). \tag{4.51}$$

When we substitute (4.50) in (4.51), we obtain the following equation for determining α_0:

$$\alpha_0 = \tfrac{64}{75} + 0.48\alpha_0 .$$

From this we get

$$\alpha_0 = 1.641025.$$

Consequently,

$$\begin{aligned} x_{10} &= 1.547692; \qquad x_{20} = 0.08; \\ x_{30} &= 1.907692; \qquad x_{40} = 1.467692. \end{aligned} \tag{4.52}$$

On the basis of formulas (4.32) and (4.33), we get as our first approximation

$$\begin{aligned} x_{11} &= 1.536492 + 0.48\alpha_1 ; \\ x_{21} &= 0.1104; \\ x_{31} &= 1.960492 + 0.48\alpha_1 ; \\ x_{41} &= 1.426092 + 0.48\alpha_1 , \end{aligned} \tag{4.53}$$

where, in accordance with (4.34),

$$\alpha_1 = \tfrac{1}{3}(x_{11} - x_{10} + x_{31} - x_{30} + x_{41} - x_{40}). \quad (4.54)$$

When we substitute (4.52) and (4.53) in (4.54), we obtain

$$\alpha_1 = 0 + 0.48\alpha_1 ,$$

from which we get $\alpha_1 = 0$.

Thus, as our first approximation, we have $x_{11} = 1.536492$, $x_{21} = 0.1104$, $x_{31} = 1.960492$, and $x_{41} = 1.426092$. This will also be obtained if we perform a simple iteration on the vector (4.52).

By continuing this process, we obtain $\alpha_n = 0$ in all the successive approximations. Consequently, the Sokolov method does not differ at all from the method of successive approximations if we take as our zeroth approximation the vector (4.52). However, we should not identify here these two methods since the radius of convergence of the method of successive approximations in the present example is 25/12, whereas the radius of convergence of the Sokolov method is 25/6 except for the point 25/12 itself, and the Sokolov method always converges better than the method of successive approximations where the latter can be used. In the present example, the eighth approximation by the Sokolov method yields $x_{18} = 1.534966$, $x_{28} = 0.122009$, $x_{38} = 1.975157$, and $x_{48} = 1.412956$.

The absolute error does not exceed unity in the sixth decimal place.

We note that to obtain the eighth approximation, we performed eight simple iterations beginning with the initial approximation (4.52); that is, the number of calculations is almost the same with both methods.

If we take an eigenvector as the coordinate function, the Sokolov method coincides with the method of L. A. Lyusternik when a sufficiently large number of iterations are made. For the present example, when eight iterations are made by Lyusternik's method, we have

$$\bar{x}_{18} = 1.534965; \qquad \bar{x}_{28} = 0.122011;$$

$$\bar{x}_{38} = 1.975159; \qquad \bar{x}_{48} = 1.412955.$$

2. Consider the system of equations of the form

$$\sum_{l=1}^{N} a_{ml}^{*} x_l = f_m \qquad (m = 1, 2, \ldots, N). \tag{4.55}$$

Let us transform this system into the form

$$\sum_{l=1}^{N} b_{ml} x_l = f_m + \sum_{l=1}^{N} d_{ml} x_l \tag{4.56}$$

so that the system of equations

$$\sum_{l=1}^{N} b_{ml} x_l = g_m{}^{*} \tag{4.57}$$

can be solved in a comparatively simple manner. It is always possible, for example, to transform the system (4.55) so that the matrix $[b_{ml}]$ will be triangular or diagonal. Then it is relatively easy to solve the system (4.57).

The Sokolov method can be applied to the system (4.56) if successive approximations are constructed as follows:

$$\sum_{l=1}^{N} b_{ml} x_{ln} = f_m + \sum_{l=1}^{N} d_{ml} x_{ln-1} + \sum_{j=1}^{N} C_{mj}^{*} \alpha_{jn} \tag{4.58}$$

$$(m = 1, 2, \ldots, N; \quad n = 1, 2, 3, \ldots),$$

where

$$C_{mj}^{*} = (d_m, \varphi_j) = \sum_{l=1}^{N} d_{ml} \varphi_{jl}, \tag{4.59}$$

and the parameters α_{nj} are determined in accordance with formula (4.34) or formulas (4.46) and (4.47).

We determine the x_{mn} from the system (4.58):

$$x_{mn} = \sum_{i=1}^{N} \beta_{im} \left\{ f_i + \sum_{l=1}^{N} d_{il} x_{ln-1} + \sum_{j=1}^{k} C_{ij}^{*} \alpha_{jn} \right\}, \tag{4.60}$$

where

$$\beta_{im} = \frac{M_{im}}{D_N}, \qquad D_N = \begin{vmatrix} b_{11} & \cdots & b_{1N} \\ \cdot & \cdots & \cdot \\ b_{N1} & \cdots & b_{NN} \end{vmatrix}$$

and M_{im} is the cofactor of the element b_{im}. If we introduce the notations

$$g_m = \sum_{i=1}^{N} \beta_{im} f_i,$$

$$a_{ml} = \sum_{i=1}^{N} \beta_{im} d_{il}, \tag{4.61}$$

the sequence (4.60) will take the form (4.32) since, according to (4.33) and (4.59),

$$C_{ms} = \sum_{i=1}^{N} \beta_{im} C_{is}^*.$$

Consequently, if $L_k(1) < 1$, the sequence (4.60) converges to the solution of the system of equations (4.55).

Formulas (4.41) and (4.42) may be used for making error estimates. However, when we calculate $L_k(1)$ and $\Omega_{sm}(1)$ from formulas (4.37) and (4.43) we need to keep in mind that the a_{ml} have the form (4.61).

In the case in which

$$b_{ml} = \begin{cases} a_{ml}^*, & m \geqslant l, \\ 0, & m < l, \end{cases} \quad d_{ml} = \begin{cases} -a_{ml}^*, & m < l, \\ 0, & m \geqslant l, \end{cases}$$

the successive approximations (4.58) are determined from the system of equations

$$\sum_{l=1}^{m} a_{ml}^* x_{ln} + \sum_{l=m+1}^{N} a_{ml}^* x_{ln-1} + \sum_{j=1}^{k} C_{mj}^* \alpha_{jn} = f_m. \tag{4.62}$$

If $k = 0$, the system (4.62) takes the form

$$\sum_{l=1}^{m} a_{ml}^* \tilde{x}_{ln} + \sum_{l=m+1}^{N} a_{ml}^* \tilde{x}_{ln-1} = f_m,$$

from which it is clear that the $\tilde{x}_{mn}$ represent the nth approximate solution of the system (4.55) obtained by Seidel's method.

It follows from Theorem 6 that if the sufficient condition for the convergence of Seidel's method is satisfied, the sequence defined by the system (4.62) converges to the solution of the system (4.55).

Example 18. Find the solution of the system of equations

$$x_1 = -0.42 + 0.20x_1 + 0.22x_2 + 0.26x_3 + 0.24x_4,$$

$$x_2 = 0.22 + 1.00x_1 - 0.02x_2 - 0.06x_3 - 0.04x_4,$$

$$x_3 = 1.20 + 0.50x_1 + 0.40x_2 - 0.03x_3 - 0.02x_4,$$

$$x_4 = -0.04 + 0.50x_1 - 0.50x_2 + 1.00x_3 + 0.02x_4$$

$$(x_1 = 1, \quad x_2 = 1, \quad x_3 = 2, \quad x_4 = 2).$$

Suppose that $k = 1$, $\varphi_1 = \{1, 1, 1, 1\}$ and $x_0 = \{0, 0, 0, 0\}$. Then, in accordance with (4.59) and (4.62), we have for our first approximation:

$$\begin{aligned} x_{11} &= -0.42 + 0.92\alpha_1; \\ x_{21} &= 0.22 + 1.00x_{11} - 0.12\alpha_1; \\ x_{31} &= 1.20 + 0.50x_{11} + 0.40x_{21} - 0.05\alpha_1; \\ x_{41} &= -0.04 + 0.50x_{11} - 0.50x_{21} + 1.00x_{31} + 0.02\alpha_1, \end{aligned} \tag{4.63}$$

where

$$\alpha_1 = \tfrac{1}{4}(x_{11} + x_{21} + x_{31} + x_{41}). \tag{4.64}$$

From the system (4.63), we obtain

$$\begin{aligned} x_{11} &= -0.42 + 0.92\alpha_1; \\ x_{21} &= -0.20 + 0.80\alpha_1; \\ x_{31} &= 0.91 + 0.73\alpha_1; \\ x_{41} &= 0.76 + 0.81\alpha_1. \end{aligned} \tag{4.65}$$

When we substitute (4.65) in (4.64), we obtain

$$4\alpha_1 = 1.05 + 3.26\alpha_1,$$

$$\alpha_1 = 1.42.$$

Consequently, for our first approximation, we have:

$$x_{11} = 0.89; \qquad x_{21} = 0.94; \qquad x_{31} = 1.95; \qquad x_{41} = 1.91.$$

The errors are 11, 6, 2.5, and 4.5%, respectively.

For our second approximation, we have:

$$x_{12} = 0.9302 + 0.92\alpha_2\,;$$
$$x_{22} = 0.0078 + 1.00x_{12} - 0.12\alpha_2\,;$$
$$x_{32} = 1.1033 + 0.50x_{12} + 0.40x_{22} - 0.05\alpha_2\,;$$
$$x_{42} = -0.0018 + 0.50x_{12} - 0.50x_{22} + 1.00x_{32} + 0.02\alpha_2,$$
$$\alpha_2 = \tfrac{1}{4}(x_{12} - x_{11} + x_{22} - x_{21} + x_{32} - x_{31} + x_{42} - x_{41}),$$

from which we obtain

$$x_{12} = 0.9302 + 0.92\alpha_2\,;$$
$$x_{22} = 0.9380 + 0.80\alpha_2\,;$$
$$x_{32} = 1.9438 + 0.73\alpha_2\,;$$
$$x_{42} = 1.9379 + 0.81\alpha_2\,;$$
$$4\alpha_2 = 0.0597 + 3.26\alpha_2\,;$$
$$\alpha_2 = 0.08.$$

Consequently,

$$x_{12} = 1.004; \qquad x_{22} = 1.002; \qquad x_{32} = 2.002; \qquad x_{42} = 2.003.$$

The errors are 0.4, 0.2, 0.1, and 0.15 %, respectively.

In the present example, $L_0(1) = 0.82$, and, consequently, Seidel's method converges, although rather slowly. For example, if for our zeroth approximation we take the first approximation obtained by the Sokolov method, then in order to obtain the second approximation of the Sokolov method, we would have to take no fewer than ten approximations with the Seidel method.

Suppose that $k = 2$, $\varphi_1 = \{1, 1, 0, 0\}$, $\varphi_2 = \{0, 0, 1, 1\}$ and $x_0 = \{0, 0, 0, 0\}$. Then, as our first approximation, we have:

$$x_{11} = -0.42 + 0.42\alpha_1 + 0.50\alpha_2\,;$$
$$x_{21} = 0.22 + 1.00x_{11} - 0.02\alpha_1 - 0.10\alpha_2\,; \tag{4.66}$$
$$x_{31} = 1.20 + 0.50x_{11} + 0.40x_{21} - 0.05\alpha_2\,;$$
$$x_{41} = -0.04 + 0.50x_{11} - 0.50x_{21} + 1.00x_{31} + 0.02\alpha_2\,;$$
$$\alpha_1 = \tfrac{1}{2}(x_{11} + x_{21}); \qquad \alpha_2 = \tfrac{1}{2}(x_{31} + x_{41}). \tag{4.67}$$

From the system (4.66), we obtain:

$$\begin{aligned} x_{11} &= -0.42 + 0.42\alpha_1 + 0.50\alpha_2 ;\\ x_{21} &= -0.20 + 0.40\alpha_1 + 0.40\alpha_2 ;\\ x_{31} &= 0.91 + 0.37\alpha_1 + 0.36\alpha_2 ;\\ x_{41} &= 0.76 + 0.38\alpha_1 + 0.43\alpha_2 . \end{aligned} \tag{4.68}$$

When we substitute (4.68) in (4.67), we obtain the following system for determining the parameters α_1 and α_2:

$$\begin{aligned} 2\alpha_1 &= -0.62 + 0.82\alpha_1 + 0.90\alpha_2 ;\\ 2\alpha_2 &= 1.67 + 0.75\alpha_1 + 0.79\alpha_2 . \end{aligned}$$

Therefore, $\alpha_1 = 1$ and $\alpha_2 = 2$.

Consequently, as our first approximation, we have:

$$x_{11} = 1; \qquad x_{21} = 1; \qquad x_{31} = 2; \qquad x_{41} = 3,$$

which coincides with the exact solution.

Example 19. The system of equations

$$\begin{aligned} 1.1260x_1 + 0.2630x_2 + 0.3117x_3 + 0.2993x_4 &= 0.1587;\\ 0.1197x_1 + 1.2548x_2 + 0.3160x_3 + 0.3095x_4 &= 0.1474;\\ 0.1006x_1 + 0.2240x_2 + 1.3218x_3 + 0.3536x_4 &= 0.1043;\\ 0.0835x_1 + 0.1898x_2 + 0.3058x_3 + 1.4209x_4 &= 0.0494, \end{aligned} \tag{4.69}$$

has the solution:

$$\begin{aligned} x_1 &= 0.103039; \qquad & x_2 &= 0.092870;\\ x_3 &= 0.054078; \qquad & x_4 &= 0.004668. \end{aligned}$$

(This example is taken from [14], p. 151.)

Let us represent the system (4.69) in the form:

$$\begin{aligned} x_1 &= 0.1587 - 0.1260x_1 - 0.2630x_2 - 0.3117x_3 - 0.2993x_4;\\ x_2 &= 0.1474 - 0.1197x_1 - 0.2548x_2 - 0.3160x_3 - 0.3095x_4;\\ x_3 &= 0.1043 - 0.1006x_1 - 0.2240x_2 - 0.3218x_3 - 0.3536x_4;\\ x_4 &= 0.0494 - 0.0835x_1 - 0.1898x_2 - 0.3058x_3 - 0.4209x_4. \end{aligned} \tag{4.70}$$

The method of successive approximations cannot be applied to the system (4.70) since one is an eigenvalue of the matrix of the coefficients on the right-hand side. Sokolov's method, however, gives good convergence.

Suppose that $k = 1$, $\varphi_1 = \{1, 1, 1, 1\}$, $\psi_1 = \{10, 22, 31, 36\}$ and $x_0 = \{0, 0, 0, 0\}$. The vector φ_1 is, as can easily be seen, an eigenvector of the matrix of the coefficients on the right-hand side of the system (4.70) and the vector ψ_1 is close to an eigenvector of the transposed matrix. Then, as our first approximation, we have, in accordance with (4.32) and (4.33):

$$x_{11} = 0.1587 - \alpha_1 ;$$

$$x_{21} = 0.1474 - \alpha_1 ;$$

$$x_{31} = 0.1043 - \alpha_1 ;$$

$$x_{41} = 0.0494 - \alpha_1 .$$

To determine the parameter α_1 on the basis of (4.46), we obtain the equation

$$(2\alpha_1 - 0.1587)\cdot 10 + (2\alpha_1 - 0.1474)\cdot 22$$
$$+ (2\alpha_1 - 0.1043)\cdot 31 + (2\alpha_1 - 0.0494)\cdot 36 = 0,$$

or

$$198\alpha_1 = 9.8415.$$

Therefore,

$$\alpha_1 = 0.0497.$$

Consequently, as our first approximation, we have:

$$x_{11} = 0.1090; \quad x_{21} = 0.0977; \quad x_{31} = 0.0546; \quad x_{41} = -0.0003.$$

If the vector ψ_1 were an exact eigenvector of the transposed matrix of the coefficients on the right-hand side of (4.70), the successive approximations could be calculated by simple iterations since all the α_n would be equal to zero. However, in this example, the vector ψ_1 is merely close to an eigenvector and the iterations involve a certain roundoff. Therefore, the α_n will differ from zero, though by quite small amounts. Their accumulation at each iteration can slow down the convergence process and, in some cases, can even make the process diverge. To avoid this contingency we need not take the α_n into account at every step; rather, after calculating n approximations by simple iterations, we should take the α_n into account at the $(n+1)$st approximation, and so forth.

For the second and third approximations obtained by simple iterations, we obtain, respectively,

$$x_{12} = 0.1023; \qquad x_{22} = 0.0923;$$

$$x_{32} = 0.0540; \qquad x_{42} = 0.0052;$$

$$x_{13} = 0.10315; \qquad x_{23} = 0.09296;$$

$$x_{33} = 0.05412; \qquad x_{43} = 0.00464.$$

For the fourth approximation, we have, on the basis of (4.32) and (4.33):

$$\begin{aligned} x_{14} &= 0.10300 - \alpha_4; \qquad & x_{34} &= 0.05404 - \alpha_4; \\ x_{24} &= 0.09283 - \alpha_4; \qquad & x_{44} &= 0.00464 - \alpha_4, \end{aligned} \tag{4.71}$$

where α_4 is determined from the equation

$$(\alpha_4 - \delta_{14})\cdot 10 + (\alpha_4 - \delta_{24})\cdot 22 + (\alpha_4 - \delta_{34})\cdot 31 + (\alpha_4 - \delta_{44})\cdot 36 = 0, \tag{4.72}$$

$$\delta_{i4} = x_{i4} - x_{i3} \qquad (i = 1, 2, 3, 4).$$

When we substitute (4.71) in (4.72), we obtain $198\alpha_4 = -0.00684$, from which we get $\alpha_4 = -0.000035$. Consequently, as our fourth approximation, we have:

$$x_{14} = 0.103035; \qquad x_{24} = 0.092865;$$

$$x_{34} = 0.054075; \qquad x_{44} = 0.004675.$$

The maximum error does not exceed 7×10^{-6}.

Bibliography

1. S. Banach, Sur les opérations dans les ensembles abstraits et leurs applications aux équations intégrales, *Fund. Math.* **3** (1922).
2. I. S. Berezin and N. P. Zhidkov, "Metody Vychisleniy" ("Computational Methods"), Vols. I, II. Fizmatgiz, Moscow, 1959.
3. S. Bleykh and E. Melan, Uravneniya v konechnykh raznostyakh statiki sooruzheniy (Finite difference equations in the statics of structures), Ob'ed. nauch-tekh DNTVU NKMP, Kharkov, 1936.
4. E. D. But, "Chislennye Metody" ("Numerical Methods"). Fizmatgiz, Moscow, 1959.
5. P. M. Varvak, Razvitie i prilozhenie metoda setok k raschetu plastinok (Development and application of the method of nets to the analysis of plates), Part I. Akad. Nauk, Ukrain. SSR, Kier, 1949.
6. I. O. Vlasov and I. A. Charnyi, Ob odnom metode chislennogo integrirovaniya obyknovennykh differentsial'nykh uravneniy (A method of numerical integration of ordinary differential equations), *Inzhen. Sb. Inst. Mekh. Akad. Nauk, USSR*, Vol. VIII. Akad. Nauk, Ukrain. SSR, 1950.
7. Yu. V. Vorob'ev, "Metod Momentov v Prikladnoy Matematike" ("Method of Moments in Applied Mathematics"). Fizmatgiz, Moscow, 1958.
8. B. G. Galerkin, Sterzhni i plastinki (Rods and plates). Ryady v nekotorykh voprosakh uprugogo ravnovesiya sterzhney i plastin, Vestnik inzhenerov i tekhnikov, No. 19, 1915.
9. B. P. Demidovich and I. A. Maron, "Osnovy Vychislitel'noy Matematiki" ("Fundamentals of Computational Mathematics"). Fizmatgiz, Moscow, 1960.
10. B. P. Demidovich, I. A. Maron and E. Z. Shuvalova, "Chislennye Metody Analiza" ("Numerical Methods of Analysis"). Fizmatgiz, Moscow, 1962.
11. L. V. Kantorovich, *Dokl. Akad. Nauk, SSSR*, No. 5 (1933).
12. L. V. Kantorovich, Nekotorye zamechaniya o metode Rittsa (Certain comments on the Ritz method), *Trudy Vyssh. Inzh.-Tekhn. Uchilishcha VMF* **3** (1941).
13. L. V. Kantorovich, Funktsional'nyy analiz i prikladnaya matematika (Functional analysis and applied mathematics), *Uspekhi Mat. Nauk* **3**, No. 6 (1948).
14. L. V. Kantorovich and V. I. Krylov, "Approximate Methods of Higher Analysis." Interscience, New York, 1959.
15. L. V. Kantorovich and G. P. Akilov, "Funktsional'nyy Analiz v Normirovannykh Prostranstvakh" ("Functional Analysis in Normed Spaces"). Fizmatgiz, Moscow, 1959.
16. R. Caccioppoli, Un teorema generale sull'esistenza di elementi uniti in una transformazione funzionale, *Rend. Accad. Lincei* **11** (1930).

17. M. V. Keldysh, O metode B. G. Galerkina dlya resheniya krayevykh zadach. (On the method of B. G. Galerkin for solving boundary-value problems), *Izv. Akad. Nauk, SSSR, Ser. Matem.* **6**, No. 6 (1942).

18. L. Collatz, "*The Numerical Treatment of Differential Equations*" (translation from the German). Berlin, 1960.

19. M. F. Kravchuk, "Zastosuvannya Sposobu Momentiv do Rozv'-yazannya Liniynykh Diferentsial'nykh ta Integral'nykh Rivnyan'" ("Application of the Method of Moments to the Solution of Linear Differential and Integral Equations"), Vid-vo Ukr. Akad. Nauk, Kiev, 1932.

20. M. F. Kravchuk, Pro zadachu momentiv (On the problem of moments), *Zh. Inst. Mat., Akad. Nauk, Ukrain. SSR*, No. 2 (1935).

21. M. A. Krasnosel'skiy, Skhodimost' metoda Galerkina dlya nelineynykh uravneniy (Convergence of Galerkin's method for nonlinear equations), *Dokl. Akad. Nauk, SSSR* **23**, No. 6 (1950).

22. M. A. Krasnosel'skiy, "Topologicheskie Metody v Teorii Nelineynykh Integral'nykh Uravneniy (Topological Methods in the Theory of Nonlinear Integral Equations). Gostekhizdat, Moscow, 1956.

23. L. E. Krivoshein, Priblizhennoe reshenie nekotorykh zadach dlya lineynykh integro-differentsial'nykh uravneniy (Approximate solution of certain problems for linear integrodifferential equations), author's abstract of a dissertation. Tashkent State University, 1958.

24. L. E. Krivoshein, Priblizhennye metody resheniya obyknovennykh lineinykh integro-differentsial'nykh uravnenii (Approximate methods of solution of ordinary linear integrodifferential equations), *Izv. Akad. Nauk, Kir. SSR*, 1962.

25. A. N. Krylov, "Lektsii o Priblizhennykh Vychisleniyakh" (Lectures on Approximate Calculations). GTTI, Moscow, 1954.

26. N. M. Krylov, Pro rizni uzagal'nennya Rittsevogo metodu ta metodu naimenshikh kvadrativ dlya nablizhenogo integruvannya rivnyan' matematichnoyi fizyky (Various generalizations of the Ritz method and the method of least squares for approximate integration of the equations of mathematical physics), *Pr. fiz.-Matem. Viddilu, Akad. Nauk, Ukrain. SSR* (1926).

27. N. M. Krylov, Mémorial des sciences math. fasc., XLIX, 1931.

28. N. M. Krylov, Priblizhennoe reshenie osnovnykh problem matematicheskoy fiziki (Approximate solution of basic problems of mathematical physics), *Izv. Akad. Nauk, Ukrain. SSR* (1931).

29. N. M. Krylov and N. N. Bogolyubov, Sur la calcul des racines de la transcendante de Fredholm, etc., *Izv. Akad. Nauk, SSSR, Ser. OMEN*, No. 5 (1929).

30. R. Courant and D. Hilbert, "Methods of mathematical physics," Vols. I and II. Interscience, New York and London, 1953–1962 (selected chapters).

31. R. Courant, K. Friedrichs and H. Lewy, Über die partiellen Differenzengleichungen der mathematischen Physik, *Math. Ann.* **100**, 32.
32. O. A. Ladyzhenskaya, Reshenie zadachi Koshi dlya giperbolicheskikh sistem metodom konechnykh raznostei (Solution of the Cauchy problem for hyperbolic systems by the method of finite differences), author's abstracts of a dissertation. Leningrad State University Press, 1949.
33. L. S. Leybenzon, "Variatsionnye metody resheniya zadach teorii uprugosti" ("Variational methods of solution of problems in the theory of elasticity"). Gostekhizdat, Moscow, 1943.
34. J. Liouville, Sur le développement des fonctions ou parties des fonctions en séries dont les divers termes sont assujettis à satisfaire à une même équation differentielle du second ordre, contenant un paramètre variable, *J. math. pur appl.* I (1836), II (1837).
35. A. Yu. Luchka, Dostatochnoe uslovie skhodimosti metoda osredneniya funktsional'nykh popravok (Sufficient condition for convergence of the method of averaging functional corrections), *Dokl. Akad. Nauk, SSSR* **122**, No. 2 (1958).
36. A. Yu. Luchka, Priblizhennoe reshenie integral'nykh uravneniy Fredgol'm metodom osredneniya funktsional'nykh Popravok (Approximate solution of Fredholm's integral equations by the method of averaging functional corrections), *UMZh* **12**, No. 1 (1960).
37. A. Yu. Luchka, Priblizhennoe reshenie lineynykh operatornykh uravnnii v prostranstve Banakha metodom Yu. D. Sokolova (Approximate solution of linear operator equations in a Banach space by the method of Yu. D. Sokolov), *UMZh* **13**, No. 1 (1961).
38. A. Yu. Luchka, Nablyzhene rozv'yazannya bezkonechnykh sistem algebraiychnykh rivnyan' metodom Yu. D. Sokolova (Approximate solution of infinite systems of algebraic equations by the method of Yu. D. Sokolov), *Dokl. Akad. Nauk, Ukrain. SSR*, No. 2 (1961).
39. A. Yu. Luchka, Pro nablyzhene rozv'yazannya liniynykh operatornykh rivnyan'v prostori Banakha metodom Yu. D. Sokolova (Approximate solution of linear operator equations in Banach spaces by the method of Yu. D. Sokolov), *Dokl. Akad. Nauk, Ukrain. SSR*, No. 4 (1961).
40. A. Yu. Luchka, O teorii i primeneniyakh metoda osredneniya funktsional'nykh popravok (Theory and applications of the method of averaging functional corrections), abstract of a dissertation for the attainment of the degree of a candidate in the physical and mathematical sciences. Akad. Nauk, Ukrain. SSR, 1961.
41. L. A. Lyusternik, Über einige Anwendungen der direkten Methoden in Variationsrechnung, *Mat. Sb.* **33** (1926).
42. L. A. Lyusternik, Zamechanie k chislennomu resheniyu krayevykh zadach uravneniya Laplasa i vychislenie sobstvennykh znachenii

metodom setok (Note on the numerical solution of the boundary-value problems of Laplace's equation and the calculation of eigenvalues by the method of nets), *Trudy Mat. Inst. Steklov* **20** (1947).

43. L. A. Lyusternik and V. I. Sobolev, ("Elements of functional analysis"). Gordon and Breach, New York, 1962.
44. G. Markus, Teoriya uprogoy setki i ee prilozhenie k raschetu plit i bezbalochnykh perekrytii (Theory of an elastic net and its application to the design of slabs and girderless floors), DNTVU, Kiev, 1936.
45. Yu. M. Molokovich, Ob odnom priblizhennom metode resheniya lineynykh integral'nykh uravneniy (Approximate method of solution of linear integral equations), *Izv. Vyssh. Uch. Zaved. Matematika* **5** p. 12 (1959).
46. B. G. Mosolov, Ob odnom priblizhennom metode resheniya nelineynogo integro-differentsial'nogo uravneniya (Approximate method of solving a nonlinear integrodifferential equation), *Izv. Akad. Nauk, UzSSR, Ser. Fiz.-Mat. Nauk*, No. 2 (1961).
47. Sh. Ye. Mikeladze, "Novye Metody Integrirovaniya Differentsial'nykh Uravneniy i ikh Prilozhenie k Zadacham Teorii Uprugosti" ("New Methods of Integration of Differential Equations and Their Application to Problems in the Theory of Elasticity"). GTTI, Moscow and Leningrad, 1951.
48. S. G. Mikhlin, "O skhodimosti metoda Galerkina" (Convergence of Galerkin's method), *Dokl. Akad. Nauk, SSSR* **61**, No. 2 (1948).
49. S. G. Mikhlin, Nekotorye dostatochnye usloviya skhodimosti metoda Galerkina (Certain sufficient conditions for the convergence of Galerkin's method), *Uch. Zap., Lenin. Gos. Univ., No. 135, Ser. Mat., Nauk*, No. 18 (1950).
50. S. G. Mikhlin, O skhodimosti metoda naimen'shikh kvadratov (Convergence of the method of least squares), *Dokl. Akad. Nauk, SSSR* **59**, No. 7 (1948).
51. S. G. Mikhlin, "Variatsionnye Metody v Matematicheskoy Fizike" ("Variational Methods in Mathematical Physics"). Fizmatgiz, Moscow, 1957.
52. S. G. Mikhlin, O ratsional'nom vybore koordinatnykh funktsiy v metode Rittsa (Correct choice of coordinate functions in the Ritz method), *Zh. Vychisl. Mat. Mat. Fiz.* **2**, No. 3 (1962).
53. S. G. Mikhlin, Metod naimen'shikh kvadratov v zadachakh matematicheskoy fiziki (Method of least squares in problems of mathematical physics), *Uch. Zap., Lenin. Gos. Univ., No. 111, Ser. Mat. Nauk*, No. 16 (1949).
54. S. G. Mikhlin, "Pryamye Metody v Matematicheskoy Fizike" ("Direct Methods in Mathematical Physics"). GTTI, Moscow and Leningrad, 1950.

55. I. P. Mysovskikh, Predstavlenie rezol'venty summy dvukh yader (Representation of the resolvent of the sum of two kernels), *Mat. Sb.* **46** (88), 1 (1958).
56. C. Neumann, "Untersuchungen über das logarithmische und Newtonische Potential." Leipzig, 1877.
57. V. V. Nemytskiy, Metod nepodvizhnykh tochek v analize (Method of stationary points in analysis), *Uspekhi Mat. Nauk* **1** (1936).
58. L. J. Paige and O. Taussky, "Simultaneous Linear Equations and the Determination of Eigenvalues." Nat. Bur. Stand. Appl. Math. Series, 29, Washington, 1953.
59. Ya. I. Perel'man, Metod B. G. Galerkina v variatsionnom ischislenii i teorii uprugosti (Method of B. G. Galerkin in the calculus of variations and elasticity theory). PMM, Vol. V, 2nd ed., 1941.
60. G. I. Petrov, Primenenie metoda Galerkina k zadache ob ustoychivosti techeniya vyazkoy zhidkosti (Application of Galerkin's method to the problem of stability of flow of a viscous liquid). PMM, Vol. IV' 3rd ed., 1940.
61. I. G. Petrovskiy, Novoe dokazatel'stvo sushchestvovaniya resheniya zadachi Dirikhle metodom konechnykh raznostey (New proof of the existence of a solution to Dirichlet's problem by the method of finite differences), *Uspekhi Mat. Nauk* **8** (1940).
62. M. Picone, Sul metodo delle minime potenze ponderate e sul metodo di Ritz per il calcolo approssimato nei problemi della fisica matematica, *Rend. Circ. Math. Palermo* **52** (1928).
63. N. I. Pol'skiy, Nekotorye obobshcheniya metoda B. G. Galerkina (Some generalizations of the method of B. G. Galerkin), *Dokl. Akad. Nauk, SSSR* **86**, No. 3 (1952).
64. W. Ritz, Über eine neue Methode zur Lösung gewisser Variations probleme der math. Physik, *J. reine ang. Math.* **135** (1908).
65. M. G. Salvadori, "*Numerical Methods in Engineering*." Prentice-Hall, New York, 1952.
66. V. Kh. Sirenko, O chislennoy realizatsii metoda osredneniya funktsional'nykh popravok (Numerical evaluation by the method of averaging functional corrections), *UMZh* **13**, No. 4 (1961).
67. V. I. Smirnov, "Kurs Vysshey Matematiki" ("Course in Higher Mathematics"), Vol. IV. GTTI, Moscow, 1953.
68. Yu. D. Sokolov, Ob odnoy zadache teorii neustanovivshikhsya dvizhenii gruntovykh vod (Problem in the theory of nonsteady motions of ground water), *Uspekhi Mat. Nauk* **5**, No. 2 (1953).
69. Yu. D. Sokolov, Pro vyznachennya dynamichnykh zusil' v shakhtnykh pidiymal'nikh kanatakh (Determination of dynamic stresses in mining hoisting cables), *Prikl. Meh.* **1**, No. 1 (1955).
70. Yu. D. Sokolov, Pro odyn metod nablyzhenogo rozv'yazannya liniynykh integral'nykh ta diferentsial'nykh rivnyan' (Method of

approximate solution of linear integral and differential equations), *Dokl. Akad. Nauk, Ukrain. SSR.* No. 2 (1955).

71. Yu. D. Sokolov, O metode osredneniya funktsional'nykh popravok (Method of averaging functional corrections), *UMZh* **9**, No. 1 (1957).
72. Yu. D. Sokolov, O primenenii metoda osredneniya funktsional'nykh popravok k nelineynym integral'nym uravneniyam (Application of the method of functional corrections to nonlinear integral equations), *UMZh* **9**, No. 4 (1957).
73. Yu. D. Sokolov, O priblizhennom reshenii lineynykh integral'nykh uravneniyakh tipa Vol'terra (The approximate solution of linear integral equations of the Volterra type), *UMZh* **10**, No. 2 (1958).
74. Yu. D. Sokolov, Ob odnom metode priblizhennogo resheniya nelineynykh integral'nykh uravneniy s peremennymi predelami (Method of approximate solution of nonlinear integral equations with variable limits), *UMZh* **10**, No. 4 (1958).
75. Yu. D. Sokolov, O primenenii metoda osredneniya funktsional'nykh popravok k lineynym otnositel'no proizvodnykh differentsial'nym uravneniyam parabolicheskogo tipa (Application of the method of functional corrections to parabolic differential equations that are linear in the derivatives), *UMZh* **12**, No. 2 (1960).
76. Yu. D. Sokolov, Ob odnom metode priblizhennogo resheniya sistem lineynykh integral'nykh uravneniy (Method of approximate solution of systems of linear integral equations), *UMZh* **13**, No. 4 (1961).
77. E. A. Chernyshenko, Isledovanie skhodimosti i ustanovlenie otsenki pogreshnosti metoda usredneniya v polnom normirovannom prostranstve (Investigation of convergence and setting up error estimates in connection with the averaging method in a complete normed space), *UMZh* **6**, No. 3 (1954).
78. E. A. Chernyshenko, O nekotorykh metodakh priblizhennogo resheniya operatornykh uravneniy (Some methods of approximate solution of operator equations), abstract of a dissertation for the attainment of the degree of Candidate in the physical and mathematical sciences. Akad. Nauk, SSSR, 1955.